CHE 327
Organic Chemistry Laboratory Manual

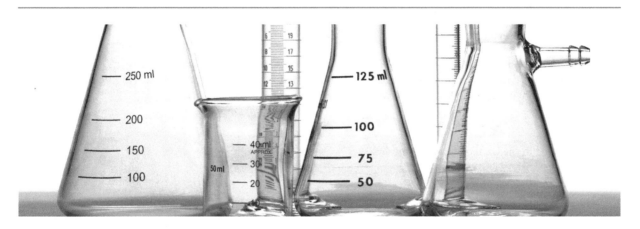

Department of Chemistry
Stony Brook University

Rong Chen
Marjorie Kandel
Zachary E. Katsamanis

2017–2018

macmillan learning
curriculum solutions

Printed in the United States of America

10 9 8 7 6 5 4 3 2 1

ISBN 978-0-7380-9829-6

Macmillan Learning Curriculum Solutions
14903 Pilot Drive
Plymouth, MI 48170
www.macmillanlearning.com

ChenR 9829-6 F17

Sustainability
Hayden-McNeil's standard paper stock uses a minimum of 30% post-consumer waste. We offer higher % options by request, including a 100% recycled stock. Additionally, Hayden-McNeil Custom Digital provides authors with the opportunity to convert print products to a digital format. Hayden-McNeil is part of a larger sustainability initiative through Macmillan Learning. Visit http://sustainability.macmillan.com to learn more.

bedford/st. martin's • hayden-mcneil
w.h. freeman • worth publishers

TABLE OF CONTENTS

Part 1 Introduction

Chapter 1   LABORATORY SAFETY

Organic chemistry laboratory is generally more dangerous than general chemistry laboratory because of the nature of organic compounds. Many of them are volatile and flammable and some are toxic. As a matter of fact, learning how to carry out experiments safely is part of the organic chemistry laboratory experience. Therefore, it is particularly important to observe strict safety rules. Disobeying safety rules can cause serious consequences – people can get seriously hurt! **Any student whose acts may endanger his or her own safety and/or that of others will not be allowed to work in the laboratory.**

1.1 Personal Protection

Students who choose to enroll in this course should realize that they will be working with a variety of substances, some of which could be irritating or hazardous with excessive exposure. For those who have chemical sensitivities, precautions such as wearing special protective garments may be necessary. Because certain substances may be teratogenic (causing malformation of an embryo or fetus) pregnant or nursing women should consult their physician in advance. Any student and/or his or her physician are welcome to discuss these concerns with the lab coordinator.

Remember, your personal safety is ultimately your responsibility – follow all the safety rules closely!

Goggles

Goggles must be worn at all times in the laboratory. Less effective eye protection such as side-shield safety glasses are not acceptable. Goggles must be in compliance with the latest Z87.1 Standard for Occupational and Educational Eye and Face Protection established by the American National Standards Institute (ANSI). 100% observance of this rule is expected.

Contact lenses will be permitted under goggles, in accordance with the latest safety recommendations of the American Chemical Society.

Heavy-Duty Gloves

Lab Safety Supply Neoprene Gloves resist a broad range of organic and inorganic chemicals. Keep the gloves in your lab drawer. Usually it is your choice whether or not to wear them, but they are required for certain experiments. Be sure to wear a glove if you have a cast or bandage, or even a small open sore on your hand. It is a good idea to wear gloves when you are cleaning glassware with acetone. To avoid transporting chemicals out of the lab area, contaminated gloves must be discarded at the end of the semester.

Sensible Clothing

Wear fitted clothing that covers your body, arms and legs, from elbow to ankle. To protect your body and clothing, a lab coat or long-sleeved cotton shirt is recommended. Natural fabrics are more resistant to solvents and are recommended. Do not wear plastic garments or jewelry, which may dissolve in solvents and adhere to your skin.

Wear flat and closed shoes that cover your entire foot in lab – no sandals, slides/mules, high-heels, platforms, or slip-ons are allowed.

Other

Artificial fingernails are a significant fire hazard. You will not be permitted to use a flame if you wear them. Since your nail situation cannot be monitored by the staff, the responsibility for your personal safety in this regard (and for make-up arrangements) is completely your own. **Confine long hair to avoid fire and contact hazards**.

1.2 Proper Laboratory Practice

You will not be allowed to begin working in the course until you sign and submit the Safety Voucher which will be distributed in lab before you perform the first experiment.

Basic Rules

- **No smoking, eating, drinking, or chewing gum is allowed in the lab.** Do not bring food or drinks into the lab work area at any time. Do not use lab glassware as containers for food or drinks.

- **No use of a cell phone is permitted in lab.**

- **No visitors are allowed without permission of the instructor.**

- **Use judgment about when to work in the hood.** For example, all work with strong corrosives, lachrymators (tear gas), foul-smelling compounds, or possible carcinogens should be done in the hood.

- **All new set-ups should be inspected by your instructor or TA before proceeding with the experiment.** Before use, examine glassware for cracks, especially star cracks in round bottom flasks. Do not force glass pieces together or apart, or into tubing.

- **Do not perform unauthorized experiments.** You may work only in a supervised lab.

- Do not leave a reaction untended. Do not take compounds out of the lab area.

- If you wish to perform an experiment that is not part of the regular series, you must submit a detailed work plan to your instructor in advance, together with safety information for all materials and apparatuses to be used.

Handling Chemicals

Before using organic solvents, check the National Fire Protection Association label cautions. A brief explanation of the NFPA code is shown in Figure 1.1 on the next page. Many organic compounds, including common solvents, are highly flammable. Do not heat these materials on a hot plate. Hot plates are to be used only in the hood. Flames are to be used only in designated areas.

Material Safety Data Sheets (MSDSs) supplied by manufacturers provide useful information. Several MSDS sources can be accessed through the undergraduate organic lab course webpage: http://www.sinc.sunysb.edu/Class/orgolab. **In the absence of specific information, treat all materials (including acetone) as if they were toxic:**

- **Avoid skin exposure.**

- **Avoid inhalation.** Do not smell the material directly; with your hand, waft the vapors toward your nose. Keep material with a high vapor pressure (low boiling point) in a beaker covered with a watch glass or in an Erlenmeyer flask. Some particularly noxious materials should be handled only in the hood. If you have breathed vapors that you judge might be harmful, notify your instructor immediately.

- **Add reagents slowly.** Add concentrated solutions to dilute ones, especially concentrated acids to water, with stirring.

- **Do not store compounds other than products in your lab drawer** unless you are told otherwise.

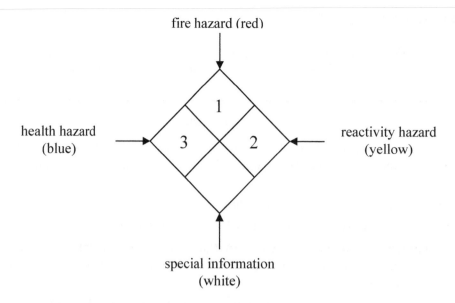

Figure 1.1 The NFPA labeling symbol. Each colored area contains a number ranging from 0-4, with 4 indicating the most severe hazard.

1.3 Disposal of Chemical Waste

Protection in the laboratory does not stop with the persons who work there. The impact on the environment should also be seriously considered. The Environmental Protection Agency (EPA) regulates waste disposal at our site. Please discard chemical substances responsibly in accordance with EPA guidelines.

There are four containers for routine waste disposal in each lab room; additional special containers will be provided as needed. Special containers will be provided for bulk silica and for other materials we want to keep segregated, such as halogenated organics, metal ions, etc.

1. *LIQUID WASTE*

   - When you are cleaning with water or liquid soap, discard the first 1-2 rinses (several milliliters each) in this container. Final water rinses, at the point where contaminants are very dilute and the glassware is essentially clean, can go down the sink.

   - Be sure to dilute concentrated acids and bases (pH less than 2 or greater than 12) before putting them into this container. **Do not put concentrated acid or base directly into the *LIQUID WASTE* container.** When performing dilutions, always add the acid or base to water, not the other way around.

   - Discard volatile organic solvents into this container. No further cleaning of the glassware is necessary if it only contained solvents.

   - Discard water-insoluble liquid substances and solutions into this container. Clean the glassware with small portions of acetone, and discard the acetone washes here also.

2. *SOLID WASTE*

   - Discard routine solid waste into this container: chemicals, filter paper, contaminated paper towels, TLC plates, boiling stones and sticks, etc.

   - Do not use this container for glass or bulk silica.

3. *GLASS*

Sweep up broken glass with the dustpan and brush, and discard them into the *BROKEN GLASS* box. If repair is possible, you may save a portion of the breakage fee.

> **Exception**: Because of the mercury hazard, if you break a thermometer or manometer, keep everyone away from the floor and/or bench area, and notify your instructor or TA. Do NOT attempt to clean it up.

4. *UNCONTAMINATED PAPER TRASH*

Use the regular trashcan for uncontaminated paper waste only. Please observe this practice for the welfare of the environment and the University cleaning staff.

1.4 Work Habits

Tidiness is essential to good lab practice, as well as safety – the cause of many accidents is a messy working area.

Avoid clutter on the bench. Only material that will be used for the experiment (such as laboratory equipment, your notebook, and the lab manual) should be left on the bench top.

Do not leave your backpack on the floor – someone may trip over it! Use the coat hooks and shelves provided for your personal belongings. You may keep food and drinks in your bag on one of the shelves.

Keep your working area clean and free of spilled chemicals or scraps of paper. Wipe up all spills immediately.

1.5 Emergencies

It is unlikely that you will have to use the safety equipment in your lab, but in the event that you do, you must know the location of all safety equipment, specifically the eye wash, shower, fire blanket, and fire extinguishers.

It is also helpful to know the location of the campus infirmary.

The following are some guidelines of what to do should an accident occur:

- Notify the instructor as soon as possible if an accident occurs. Many injuries will require first aid or medical attention. Accident reports must be filed for even small injuries.

- For burning clothing or large chemical spills on the body, walk to the shower immediately. For a spill, you may need to remove contaminated clothing under the shower.

- For a splash or vapors in the eye, flush immediately with large amounts of water; hold the eye open during washing.

- For a spill on the skin over a small area, or a small burn, wash immediately and thoroughly with cold running water at the sink. Check with your instructor to find out if further treatment is necessary

- For large chemical spills on the bench or floor, immediately alert your neighbors and the instructor, and clean up as directed.

- Small fires may be smothered by covering with an inverted beaker or watch glass. For a larger fire, call the instructor immediately. If necessary, evacuate the room, sound the alarm, and call the fire department.

- In case of an explosion, turn off heaters and evacuate the room.

- Apply direct pressure to cuts, large or small.

1.6 References

1. *Safety in Academic Chemistry Laboratories* revised 6th edition. American Chemical Society, 1995.

2. Fessenden, R. J.; Fessenden, J. S.; Feist. P. *Organic Laboratory Techniques* 3rd edition. Brooks Cole, 2001.

3. Mohrig, J. R.; Hammond, C. N.; Schatz, P. F.; Morrill, T. C. *Techniques in Organic Chemistry* W. H. Freeman and Co., 2003.

SUBMIT THIS COPY

SAFETY VOUCHER

1. I have attended the lab safety lecture.

2. I have read the lab safety instructions in the current Lab Manual.

3. I have purchased chemical splash goggles that meet ANSI Z87.1 standards. I understand that **goggles must be worn at all times in lab**. I understand that the goggles policy will be strictly adhered to.

    If it applies to me, I will observe the lab contact lens policy.

4. For personal protection, I will wear sensible clothing (and shoes) and tie back long hair.

5. I understand that artificial fingernails are not permitted for experiments involving flames.

    If I wear them, I will either remove them before the relevant experiments, or make alternate experimental arrangements as per the Laboratory Safety in my lab manual.

6. I have purchased heavy-duty gloves to be worn at certain times in lab.

7. I understand that I shall keep my own working area and the laboratory clean, and dispose of waste following the instructions.

8. I understand that I must **immediately** report all accidents and injuries, no matter how minor, to my laboratory instructor(s), that is, the teaching assistant(s) in the laboratory at the time. An accident report must be filed, and the course instructor and lab coordinator should also be notified.

9. I understand that I will not be permitted to work in lab until this form has been completed and submitted. I understand that I will be required to leave the laboratory if I do not follow the accepted safety practices.

_____

Course and section

SOLAR ID#

_____

Last Name (print legibly)

First Name (print legibly)

_____

Signature

Date

KEEP THIS COPY

SAFETY VOUCHER

1. I have attended the lab safety lecture.

2. I have read the lab safety instructions in the current Lab Manual.

3. I have purchased chemical splash goggles that meet ANSI Z87.1 standards. I understand that **goggles must be worn at all times in lab**. I understand that the goggles policy will be strictly adhered to.

    If it applies to me, I will observe the lab contact lens policy.

4. For personal protection, I will wear sensible clothing (and shoes) and tie back long hair.

5. I understand that artificial fingernails are not permitted for experiments involving flames.

    If I wear them, I will either remove them before the relevant experiments, or make alternate experimental arrangements as per the Laboratory Safety in my lab manual.

6. I have purchased heavy-duty gloves to be worn at certain times in lab.

7. I understand that I shall keep my own working area and the laboratory clean, and dispose of waste following the instructions.

8. I understand that I must **immediately** report all accidents and injuries, no matter how minor, to my laboratory instructor(s), that is, the teaching assistant(s) in the laboratory at the time. An accident report must be filed, and the course instructor and lab coordinator should also be notified.

9. I understand that I will not be permitted to work in lab until this form has been completed and submitted. I understand that I will be required to leave the laboratory if I do not follow the accepted safety practices.

_____   _____
Course and section   SOLAR ID#

_____   _____
Last Name (print legibly)   First Name (print legibly)

_____   _____
Signature   Date

9

Chapter 2   THE   NOTEBOOK

An accurate record of your experimental procedure, results, observations, and conclusions is an indispensable part of scientific work. Human memory is faulty and unreliable, so a written record of results is necessary for future reference. Even with experience, you never know in advance exactly which pieces of information will be useful. For this reason, you should strive to make your notebook as complete as possible. Furthermore, your notebook should be written so that it is intelligible to anyone who might need to repeat the work. The information might also serve as the basis for a scientific paper or a patent claim.

In CHE 327, you are required to use a bound notebook whose pages have been pre-numbered by the manufacturer. Each page should have a removable duplicate so that on alternate sheets you can make carbon copies of everything you write in lab.

2.1 Keeping the Notebook

Notes before Lab

For each experiment you should write a pre-lab in your notebook. The pre-lab write-up is evidence that you are adequately prepared to perform the experiment. It does not have to be lengthy or elaborate. In appropriate cases, the pre-lab should include procedures in the form of a step-by-step work plan (the format used in this lab manual is required; see the sample below).

Notes in Lab

Each page should have a title, your name and the date of the actual performance of the work. Pages must be properly dated so that date-dependent information (for example, water absorption on a humid day) can be tracked.

You should record the following while an experiment is in progress:

1) any adjustment to the pre-lab procedure

2) raw experimental data

3) up-to-the-minute observations

4) conclusions which will impact an immediate procedure decision

All in-lab notebook entries MUST BE MADE DIRECTLY INTO YOUR NOTEBOOK. Do not write down observations on a separate piece of paper so that you can transfer it neatly into your notebook later. Keep your notebook with you at your bench; take it to the balance and to the instrument rooms.

A sample is given below in the two-column format we require.

Name: Manny Katsamanis **Experiment:** Ester Synthesis **Date:** 03/18/2009 **TA:** Rose White	
1) Add 10-15 ml 8% aqueous $NaHCO_3$ to HCl layer. [*This is a plan for procedure and measurement.*]	Volume $NaHCO_3$ = 15 ml. At first lots of bubbling, which disappeared after 5 min. constant vigorous stirring. [*These are data, observations and an addition to the procedure.*]
2) Test solution with red litmus; should be basic. [*This is a plan and a prediction.*]	Red litmus $\rightarrow$ blue, so it is basic. [*The observation leads to a conclusion that is required before proceeding to the next step.*]

written before lab   written in lab

Data and observations should not be changed unless an error is made or the experiment repeated. Even then, the original notation should be crossed out legibly in case it needs to be retrieved. Do not use any whiting-out correction fluid, which would obscure the original.

> **Example**: ~~No change in the yellow solution~~ Formation of a yellow precipitate after 5 minutes.

Information that you forgot to enter into your notebook on a particular date cannot be added later. Making a notebook entry after lab may be treated as academic dishonesty. However, in some cases it is practical for you to make new observations or repeat experimental steps on another lab date and then enter the new information at that time.

Optional Contents

You should write procedure, data, and observations as you perform the lab work so as to ensure your record's greatest possible accuracy and integrity. On the other hand, you can generally make your interpretations and do your calculations at a later time, and change them if you discover them to be erroneous. Consistent with this distinction, material such as the following is not required to be in your notebook; if you choose to include it, you do not need to submit the carbon copies in lab (see section 2.2).

- Calculations of percent recoveries and yields, R_f values, etc.

- Conclusions that do not affect procedure. For example, you may decide to wait to interpret your spectroscopic data after lab; it is your choice whether or not to include this information in your notebook. However, certain conclusions that affect a procedure decision, such as the interpretation of a litmus test, must be recorded as you work.

- Answers to pre- and post-lab study questions.

Scientific Integrity

Recording work in progress keeps you honest. You must try to regard all information without prejudice: This means you should **record all trials**, whether they "work" or not, whether the data are "correct" or not. An inexperienced lab worker sometimes waits for "good" results before making an entry. This inappropriate practice may approach scientific dishonesty.

A good notebook will contain a certain amount of information that will later be rejected. This is not a reason for concern. Selection of the most valid or relevant data can and should come at an evaluation stage after the experimental work has been completed.

More about Keeping the Lab Record

For the part of your notebook to be kept in lab, all entries should be made directly into it and not copied from another source. **Never record elsewhere information that belongs in the notebook** – neither on handy scraps of paper, margins of the lab manual, nor on any other convenient surface. **Never temporarily memorize information** for later transcription into the notebook. In addition to introducing errors into your lab record, such disregard for accepted lab practice will make a negative impression on your lab supervisors.

As described in more detail in section 2.2, the carbon copies of the original notebook pages should be submitted at the end of each lab period. These carbon copies must exactly duplicate the originals, and for this reason you should not make pen or pencil notations on them, which will be treated as academic dishonesty.

Students are often concerned about the appearance of their notebook. You should realize that legibility and comprehensibility are essential, and for these a certain degree of neatness and organization is necessary. A Table of Contents at the beginning is a useful organizational aid; and it also helps if you leave blank pages for insertions between experiments. If all information is up to date and easily retrievable by you or another worker, you do not need to expend additional effort in making your notebook more attractive.

Your notebook serves as a record of your own work. As such, it is a unique document. **You are welcome to consult another student's notebook before or after lab, but do not bring it to lab with you**. Such action will be treated as academic dishonesty.

2.2 Evaluating the Notebook

The pre-lab write-up is evidence that you are adequately prepared to do the experiment. Early in the lab period, **your pre-lab will be checked** by one of the TAs. If the preparation is inadequate, you must obtain the required information before you can continue working.

The notebook grade will be based on your in-lab record. We are interested in the answers to two questions: 1) Was the body of the notebook written in lab as close in time as possible to the performance of the experiment? 2) Is it an intelligible, complete record of procedure, data, observations, and essential conclusions? If you write as you work, and if you try to include the essential information, you should be successful with your notebook even if you have experimental problems.

The following is how we answer the two questions. Please take care to understand and follow our procedures so that your grade will reflect the quality of your work.

1) Was the notebook written in lab along with the experiment?

- **Submit carbon copies of all new notebook entries at the end of each lab period you work**, including make-up.

- **Submit all carbons on which you have written during the lab period, even if you haven't finished the experiment, or if a page is only partially completed**. This means that occasionally you will have to split the pre-lab work plan and the corresponding data/observations between two different pages. You should leave blank pages between experiments for this purpose. Use a notation such as "continued on page xx" to keep your material organized. In other words, **do not put work from more than one date on any page**.

- **Do not go back to add to or change a previously submitted page** – such new entries cannot be graded. In some cases, this action will be seen as an attempt to alter the record and thus be treated as academic dishonesty.

- In order for your carbons to be sorted easily, **put both your TA's and your names on each page and staple the pages together in numerical order**.

- **On each page, write the complete date of submission (including the year)**. This action serves as your guarantee that the notebook pages were written during the same lab period the experimental work was done. Take care to record the date accurately.

- Put the carbons in the white box reserved for carbon copies.

- You do not need to submit carbons for pages written after lab, for example, calculations you do at home.

2) Are the contents of the notebook intelligible and complete?

To check the contents, there will be notebook questions solely on procedure, data, observations, and conclusions you should be recording. You will consult your notebook to answer the questions, but the grader will consult the carbon copies.

For the first experiment, the notebook will not be graded. Instead, there will be a self-check after the first week to help you identify problems in record keeping before you go on.

Chapter 3   GENERAL LABORATORY EQUIPMENT

There is a wide variety of equipment used in organic laboratory, including an assortment of glassware, non-glass equipment, and heating equipment. Many items are available in the student laboratory drawer, and some are community equipment which will be shared.

3.1 Glassware

Figure 3.1 on page 11 shows the glassware commonly used in an organic laboratory.

Glassware with ground-glass joints, such as round-bottom flasks, condensers, and adapters, is called standard-taper glassware. It is convenient to use because the glassware of the same standard taper may be assembled in many configurations. In addition, the ground-glass joints provide a good seal, which is desirable for many organic reactions.

However, there is one disadvantage of ground-glass joints – their tendency to stick. A thin film of grease on the joints can prevent sticking. When assembling standard-taper glassware, grease the inner joint lightly and insert it into the outer joint; then rotate the joints to distribute the grease evenly to form a thin film. Too much grease may contaminate the contents of the glassware.

Glassware with ground-glass joints is expensive. If you break this type of glassware, check with your instructor before you decide to discard it, and see if the joint can be recycled.

Safety Precautions

Before using any glassware in an experiment, check carefully for cracks or chips. Note that glassware with spherical surfaces, such as round-bottom flasks, can develop small star-shaped cracks. Replace any damaged glassware. When cracked glassware is heated, it can break or even explode in some rare cases, and therefore, cause a serious accident.

Cleaning Glassware

In all washing procedures, several small rinses (a few milliliters each) will be more effective than the same total volume in larger portions. Rinse a piece of glassware with a small amount of solvent, and swirl to coat the entire inside surface. Repeat this step if necessary. In addition to its effectiveness, this method has the virtue of conserving solvent and generating less waste.

If water alone will get your glassware clean, then this is the method of choice. Dispose of initial water-washes in the *LIQUID WASTE* container – see "Disposal of Chemical Waste" (section 1.3).

For materials that are not water-soluble, acetone may be a good cleaning agent. Acetone $(CH_3)_2C=O$ is a small molecule with both polar and nonpolar groups. Acetone's dual character enables it to solubilize materials of varying properties. It is also quite volatile (boiling point 56 $^{\circ}C$) so that glassware cleaned with acetone dries relatively quickly. Acetone can be re-used in portions to clean more than one piece of glassware. Dispose of all the washes in the *LIQUID WASTE* container.

Stubborn residues must be scrubbed. Brushes and liquid soap are available. Keep in mind that all glassware is more easily cleaned if it is done after use as soon as possible. If you have genuinely tried to clean your glassware and failed, take the dirty piece(s) to the stockroom for replacement. This is a last resort.

Glassware containing only a residue of volatile organic solvent does not need further cleaning.

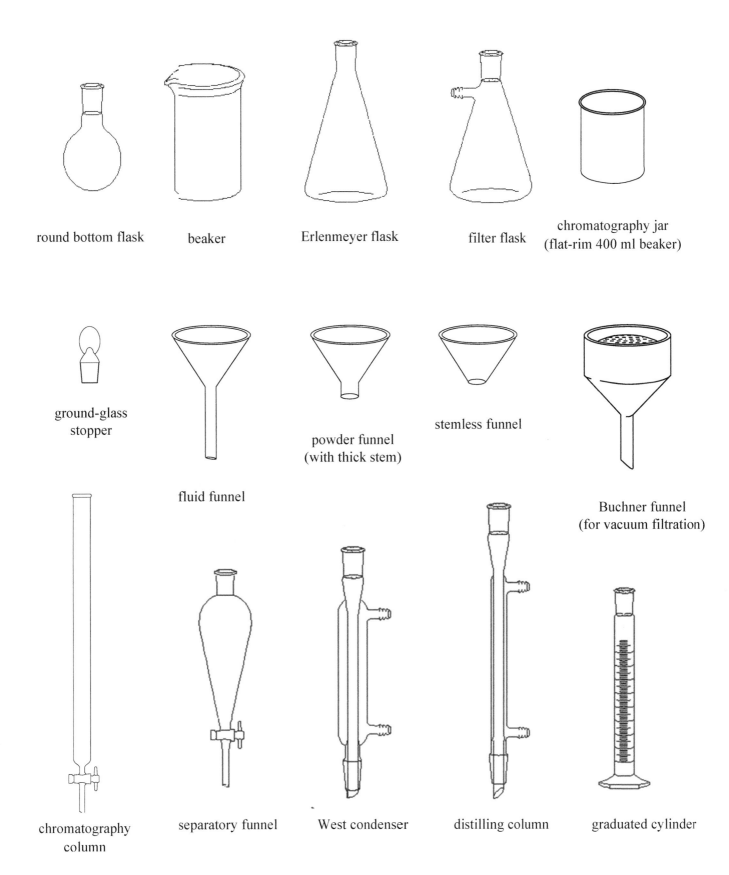

round bottom flask   beaker   Erlenmeyer flask   filter flask   chromatography jar (flat-rim 400 ml beaker)

ground-glass stopper

fluid funnel   powder funnel (with thick stem)   stemless funnel   Buchner funnel (for vacuum filtration)

chromatography column   separatory funnel   West condenser   distilling column   graduated cylinder

Figure 3.1 Glassware commonly used in an organic laboratory (continued on the next page).

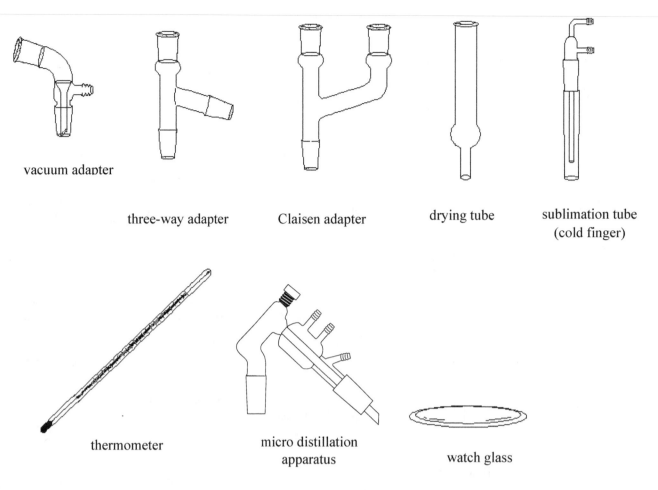

vacuum adapter

three-way adapter   Claisen adapter   drying tube   sublimation tube (cold finger)

thermometer   micro distillation apparatus   watch glass

Figure 3.1 (continued)

Drying Glassware

It is best to clean the glassware the week before and allow it to air-dry, so that it will be ready for use the following lab period.

Glassware containing only a residue of volatile organic solvent such as acetone will air-dry fairly quickly. Do not attempt to blow-dry acetone-rinsed glassware with the lab compressed air as the airlines often contain greasy dirt which undoes your cleaning.

It is often unnecessary for glassware to be dry but necessary for it to be free of water and acetone. In such a case, the glassware may be rinsed with an appropriate solvent before use. Be sure that the solvent is miscible with the residual water or acetone; use the minimum amount that will accomplish the purpose (no more than a few milliliters); and discard this solvent in the *LIQUID WASTE* container.

3.2 Non-Glass Equipment

Figure 3.2 shows some non-glass equipment that is often used in an organic laboratory.

The filtervac is a conical rubber adapter that is used to attach a Buchner funnel to a filter flask. The filter adapter is the piece that is used to stopper a trap in a vacuum filtration. Clamps and iron rings support glassware. The test-tube holder is designed to hold a test-tube and is too weak to hold a beaker or Erlenmeyer flask.

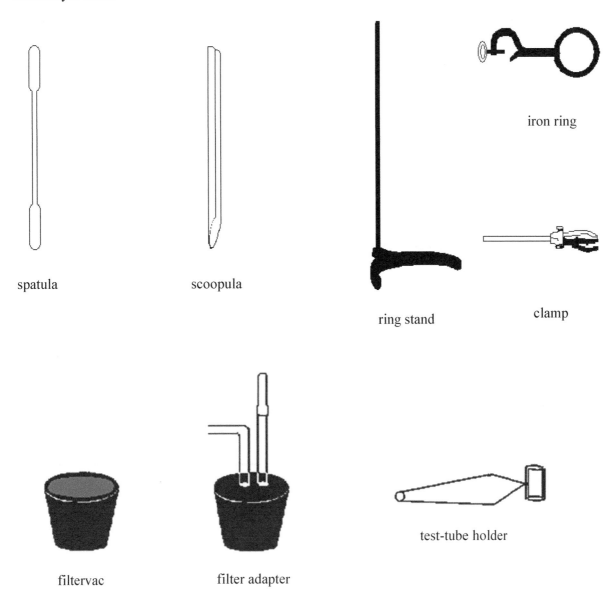

spatula   scoopula

iron ring

ring stand   clamp

filtervac   filter adapter   test-tube holder

Figure 3.2 Non-glass equipment that is often used in organic laboratory.

3.3 Heating Equipment

Some commonly used heating equipment in an organic laboratory is shown in Figure 3.3 on p.14.

The steam bath is the safest heating equipment to use in the organic laboratory. It does not generate an open flame, like Bunsen burners do. The heat comes from the steam and only reaches the maximum of about 90-95 °C; therefore, it will not overheat as heating mantles sometimes do. It is very useful for heating low-boiling solvents, especially flammable ones.

The heating mantle is one of the most commonly used heating devices in organic laboratory (others include steam bath and hot plate). It is designed to heat the contents of a round-bottom flask. There are two major types of heating mantle available commercially. One type consists of soft fiberglass; each mantle fits a specific size (that is, the heating mantle sized for a 100 ml flask will not fit any other size). The other type has a metal exterior while the inside well can be either hard ceramic or soft fiberglass. It can be used not only for the flask of designated size, but also for smaller sizes. For convenience and safety, the heating mantle is often supported by an iron ring or a labjack underneath.

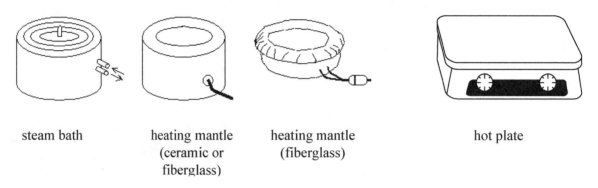

| steam bath | heating mantle (ceramic or fiberglass) | heating mantle (fiberglass) | hot plate |

Figure 3.3 Heating devices.

The electric plug of a heating mantle should be plugged into a variable transformer (or rheostat), such as a Variac, or other type of controller – never the standard wall socket – to adjust the voltage, and thus, the rate of heating.

Hot plates work well for heating flat-bottomed containers like beakers and Erlenmeyer flasks. However, **they are not recommended for heating flammable solvents because the very hot surfaces of the hot plates may be a fire hazard**.

Safety Precautions

- Never heat to dryness.
- Never plug the heating mantle into the wall socket.
- Do not use a heating mantle that appears worn.
- Never light a burner if there is flammable solvent nearby.

3.4 Other Equipment

Electronic top-loading balances, as shown in Figure 3.4, read to three decimal places and are widely used in modern organic laboratories. They are expensive and delicate precision instruments. Treat them with care. If anything (solid or liquid) spills on or near the balance, clean it immediately to avoid the corrosion from the spilled chemical. A milligram balance usually has a draft shield. While a sample is being weighed, this shield should be closed to prevent air draft from disturbing the weighing pan.

No chemical should be weighed directly on the balance pan – always weigh in a glass container (a vial or beaker), in a plastic weighing boat, or on a piece of weighing paper. The mass of the container or weighing paper will be tared (subtracted) by pressing the tare (zero) bar in the front of the balance before the sample is added. If the mass of the container is not tared, it should be determined and recorded separately and subtracted in a later calculation. If a volatile liquid is weighed, a cap or cork for the container should be used so that the sample will not evaporate during the weighing process. The mass of the cap or cork should also be included in the tare.

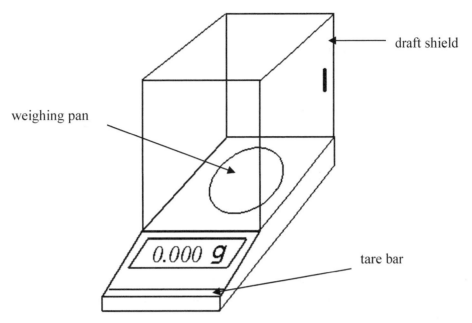

Figure 3.4 An electronic top-loading balance with draft shield.

Example: How to weigh out approximately 3.00 grams of sodium chloride.

1. Place a glass container or a piece of weighing paper on the balance pan and press the tare bar. The numerical readout will be "0.000" on the digital display. If the balance shows two decimal places, press the tare bar again.

2. Use a spatula to add small portions of sodium chloride until the desired mass is shown on the display. (Note that any amount between 2.950 and 3.049 grams can be considered approximately 3.00 grams.) **Record the precise amount in the notebook, to three decimal places.**

Other larger and more complex equipment, such as the rotary evaporator and melting-point instrument, will be discussed in other chapters.

Chapter 4   LABORATORY POLICIES

4.1 Lateness

Arriving Late to Lab

Arriving late to lab is poor practice. Important information is given at the beginning of lab through announcements and demonstrations by your instructor or TA. You are still responsible for any information that you missed as a result of your lateness. Furthermore, arriving late to lab habitually will negatively affect your technique grade.

If you arrive to lab after 30 minutes from the scheduled start of your lab session, you will be automatically considered absent and will not be permitted to perform the experiment.

Late Reports, Products, and Notebook Quizzes

To evaluate the timeliness of your notebook, and to be fair in comparing your products, results, and reports to those of other students, we must have a lateness policy.

The due dates are listed in the course schedule file. Late reports, products, and/or notebook quizzes should be submitted to your TA the following lab period with the Late Product/Result Form (p. 23). There will be a 10% grade penalty for all materials submitted within a week of the due date. **One week after the posted due date is the absolute deadline for submission of a report, product and/or a notebook quiz.** If you are absent from lab the day that a report, product, or notebook quiz is due, you will be allowed to submit the materials the following lab period, but it must be submitted by the absolute deadline.

After materials are returned, grading information will be posted on Blackboard.

Notebook Carbon Copy Violations

All carbon copies of new notebook entries, properly dated, must be turned in at the end of every lab period you work, including make-up, even if you have not finished the experiment or if a page is only partially completed. **It is our policy to deduct course total points for pages that are incorrectly dated, undated, contain notations made in pen or pencil on the carbon copy, or received late.** The amount of points deducted depends upon the nature of the violation. If a violation is committed, a carbon copy violation form will be given to you the following lab period stating the nature of the violation, as well as the amount of points deducted from your course total. **You should endeavor to be diligent with submitting carbon copies of each notebook page with the proper date and your name on time.**

4.2 Absence

Absence from Lab

If you are absent one time during the semester, you will make it up by attending the CHE 327 make-up session. **Note that the lab exercise in the make-up period is different from the missed one(s).** No special documentation is required for the first absence. However, you should confirm with the coordinator in advance to make sure the grades of the make-up experiment are recorded properly.

In unusual circumstances, permission for a second or late make-up might be granted; you must provide documents and see the lab coordinator to arrange the details.

Absence from lab does not excuse you from learning the theories and concepts about the experiment. You still need to read the lab manual and study the lecture notes so that you can do well in the theory quiz.

Absence from a Theory Quiz

The theory quiz(s) should be made up at the end of the semester as shown on the course schedule. No matter which quiz you miss, you will take the same cumulative theory make-up quiz.

There is no make-up for the "clicker" quizzes given during lecture.

4.3 Regrade

The grading scheme for each report and quiz will be posted by the end of the week that the report or quiz is returned to you. You should review the grading scheme carefully. If there is a grader's error, you can have your work re-evaluated by the lab coordinator by following the procedure on the Regrade Form (p. 25). Make a copy of the form for submission, rather than tearing the one provided in this manual. If your concerns are legitimate and clearly presented, they will be given every consideration.

All reports and quizzes should be written in indelible ink to be accepted for a regrade. **No paper (either a quiz or a product sheet) will be considered for a regrade if the paper in question is written in pencil or erasable pen.** Also, be sure to observe the regrade deadline on the grading scheme for each report/quiz. **Regrade requests that are submitted past the regrade deadline will not be considered.**

If you do not understand how the posted grading explanations apply to your work, you may wish to discuss the problem with the lab coordinator during office hours. However, such discussion is not required. If you disagree with the grading scheme, you should see the lab coordinator to discuss the issue instead of filing for a regrade.

4.4 Appeals and Miscellaneous Problems

Most of the common problems have been discussed above, and we will follow our own rules in dealing with them. However, situations may arise which might require special consideration. These include an unavoidable loss of a product caused by another student accidentally. If such an incident occurs during lab, notify your TA or instructor immediately.

If you have a problem of this sort that you would like us to consider, please see the lab coordinator during office hours and submit an Appeal Form (p. 27). (S)he will keep a record of your appeal on file. Appropriate grade adjustments will be made at the end of the course.

4.5 Stockroom Policies

You will check in glassware and equipment, which you will keep in an assigned drawer. At the end of the semester, you should return the drawer and its contents clean and in the condition you received them (other than expendables such as litmus paper). Failing to check out before the course ends will result in a fee, including the cost of: 1) the examination of the drawer by lab staff, 2) the replacement of damaged equipment, if any.

Equipment you borrow should be returned to the stockroom as soon as practical during the same lab period. Keep in mind that the stockroom closes fifteen minutes before the scheduled end of the lab period. If the stockroom is closed so that you cannot return the borrowed equipment, you should lock it in your drawer. If the equipment is still in your drawer the next period, be sure to return it promptly.

CHE 327   LATE PRODUCT/ RESULT FORM

Student's name_____   TA's name_____

Section _____   Lab room_____   Bench #_____

Title of work being submitted_____ Today's date _____

If you omit any of the important steps below, your request may not be properly understood or processed. After review, your product/result form will be returned, but this form will be retained by the lab coordinator.

Note: This form is not for handing in late carbon pages! No product/result will be accepted after the lab closing time on the final date posted in grading scheme.

1. Make a photocopy of this blank form so that you will have another in case of later need. You can also download it from Blackboard.

2. If you are submitting several pieces of work at the same time, **each must have its own form.**

3. Be sure you filled in the locating information correctly at the top of this sheet so that a CHE 27 staff member can gather your vial from your drawer after the lab is over.   Be sure the vial is properly labeled.

4. Complete this form and staple it to the front of the product/result sheet being submitted, and deposit the packet in the red box in the stockroom.

CHE 327   REGRADE FORM

Student's name_____   **TA's name**_____

Course #_____   **Section #**_____   **Lab #**_____   **Bench #**_____

Title of work being appealed _____   **Date submitted**_____

If you omit any of the important steps below, your request may not be properly understood or processed. After review, your paper will be returned but this form will be retained by the lab coordinator.

Note: **This form is to be used only in the case of a grader's error**. If there has been no error, but you have a special excuse for a problem that has affected your grade, you should see the lab coordinator during office hours before the posted final date. **No paper (either a quiz or a product sheet) will be considered for a regrade if the paper in question is written in pencil or erasable pen.**

1. Make a photocopy of this blank form so that you will have another in case of later need. You can also download it from the Blackboard.

2. If you are submitting several pieces of work at the same time, **each must have its own form.**

3. Complete the form and staple it to the front of the original work being submitted.

4. To keep for your own records, make a photocopy of the packet you prepared in 3).

5. **Your entire submission will be re-evaluated**, with a possible lowering of credit. Be sure to check the grading standards, which are posted on Blackboard, before requesting a regrade.

6. **You must submit your regrade before lab closing time on the posted final date. The regrade request received after the deadline will not be processed.**

7. Submit all paperwork to the red box in the stockroom.

What is the reason for this regrade request? *Explain briefly, clearly, and unemotionally.*

Original Grade _____   Regrade _____

CHE 327   APPEAL FORM

Student's name_____   TA's name_____

Course #_____   Section #_____   Lab #_____   Bench #_____

Title of work being appealed _____   Date submitted_____

Note: This form is to be used **only in the case of appeal**. If there has been a grader's error, you should file a Regrade Form.

Follow these instructions. **If you omit any of the important steps, your request may not be properly understood or processed.** At the end of the semester, your appeal will be evaluated and appropriate grade adjustment, if any, will be made.

1) If you are submitting several pieces of work at the same time, **each must have its own form.**
2) Complete the form and staple it to the front of the original work being submitted.
3) To keep for your own records, make a photocopy of the packet you prepared in 3).

What is the reason for this appeal? *Explain briefly, clearly and unemotionally.*

Chapter 5   HOW TO SUCCEED IN CHE 327

Organic chemistry laboratory courses at Stony Brook, including CHE 327 and CHE 383-384, are not only intense but also challenging in a way that is different from many lecture courses. Nevertheless, many students, including some students who are concurrently taking CHE 321, (Organic Chemistry Part 1) and have not acquired a broad knowledge of organic chemistry, finish the laboratory courses with satisfactory grades. Here are some tips.

Learn All the Important Background Information

Read Chapters 1-4 of this lab manual carefully and study the following:

- **Laboratory safety** (Chapter 1). There are also specific precautions for each experiment that you should read.
- **The Notebook** (Chapter 2).
- **Laboratory equipment** (Chapter 3).
- **Laboratory cleanup** and **disposal of hazardous waste** (Chapters 1 and 3).
- **Laboratory policies** (Chapter 4).

In addition, **read the syllabus carefully and become familiar with all the important dates. A significant amount of course total points can be obtained by simply following our policies and directions.** Sometimes the difference between two overall grades can be from lost "free" points (such as not properly labeling a vial containing the product you submit).

Prepare for Lab

- **Read before lecture to a have better understanding of the concepts explained in class**. The reading assignments for each experiment are given in this manual.
- Study the pre- and post-lab questions in the lab manual. Quiz questions might be there!
- **Go over the experiment procedure briefly while writing the pre-lab**. Make a list of instructions or a flowchart. If you are concerned about your laboratory skills, start preparing for lab early in order to have enough time to go over the experiment procedures with an instructor in his/her office hours.
- **Finish the report sheet at home**. The notebook carbon copies are due at the end of each lab period. Do not use your limited lab time on something that does not have to be done in lab.

Keep a Good Lab Notebook

The notebook quizzes count for nearly a fourth of the course grade total. These points can be easily obtained by keeping a complete and up-to-date lab notebook. Some sample notebook quizzes are posted on Blackboard. (Obviously, to gain the benefit, you must do this before doing the experiment.)

Here is a brief summary of what is required on the notebook carbon copies and what is not:

Required ----

- **Experimental procedure.** A work plan should be prepared before lab (pre-lab write-up). The details, such as the actual amount of the reagents and any adjustment of the plan, must be written in lab.
- **Observations, raw data, and everything worth noting while conducting the experiment**.
- **The complete date of submission including the year.** The submission date should be the day that the experiment (or part of the experiment) was performed.
- **The conclusions on which an immediate procedural decision is based.** For example, when you use litmus paper to test the acidity/basicity of a solution, an immediate conclusion must be drawn so that you can decide what to do next.

Not required ----

- Most calculations, such as the determination of R_f values and the percent yield, are not required – they may be done after lab.
- General conclusions of an experiment.
- Answers to the study questions.

Plan Lab Time Well

- There are only four hours in each lab period. Spending lab time efficiently enables you to finish the experiment on time and avoid late notebook carbon pages. This is particularly important as the semester proceeds when experiments become more complicated and difficult.
- **Always allow enough time at the end of each lab period for cleaning the glassware so that it has time to dry for the next lab period.**
- There will be times when standing and waiting and watching a reaction are required. While waiting, why not prepare for the next step? Obtain needed reagents (provided the reaction can be left unattended; otherwise, ask your neighbor to keep an eye on it), set up/lay out glassware and review the next step.

Do Not Fall Behind Schedule

- **Try your best not to miss a lab**. Fitting a make-up into your already busy schedule is painful.

Use the Course Resources

- Go to office hours to clarify concepts and discuss the techniques and experiments.
- Emails are useful when the posted office hours are not convenient for you. All the students and staff members in CHE 327 can email each other by using Blackboard.
- **Check Blackboard for all the course information**, including the syllabus, course schedule, latest notices, important forms, lecture notes, grade schemes, and sample quizzes.

Part 2 Techniques

Chapter 6   DISTILLATION

Distillation is a technique for separating two or more liquids whose boiling points are sufficiently different. It is often used for purifying a liquid or separating different components of a liquid mixture. Occasionally, this technique can also be used to remove a solvent from a solution.

In the process of distillation, a liquid is vaporized from one container, then condensed back to a liquid (called distillate), and collected in a separate container. When there are only one or two vaporizations and condensations occurring in the distillation process, it is called **simple distillation**. If the vaporizations and condensations occur repeatedly, it is called **fractional distillation**. Fractional distillation is much more effective in separating mixtures, especially when the boiling point difference between different components is small.

6.1 Boiling Point

The **boiling point** of a pure liquid is defined as the temperature at which its vapor pressure equals the external pressure on the surface of the liquid (usually at ambient atmospheric pressure). For instance, when a pure liquid is heated in an open container, its vapor pressure will rise as the temperature of the liquid rises. When the vapor pressure reaches atmospheric pressure, the liquid starts to boil. The boiling point of the liquid can be measured as it distils.

The boiling point of a liquid is dependent on the atmospheric pressure and is lowered when atmospheric pressure is reduced. The **normal boiling point** reported in literature references is measured under normal atmospheric pressure (1 atm, or 760 torr, or 760 Hgmm). However, on any particular day, the atmospheric pressure in the laboratory may deviate from normal. For this reason, and also due to possible thermometer error, you should allow for some deviation between your observed boiling point and the reported value.

Different liquids boil at different temperatures (under the same external pressure) because each has its own characteristic vapor pressure. Remember that a lower vapor pressure corresponds to a higher boiling point. The boiling point of a compound also reflects its molecular structure, more exactly, the type of noncovalent intermolecular interactions (such as dipole-dipole interactions and hydrogen bonding interactions). Polar compounds usually have higher boiling points than nonpolar compounds of similar molecular weight because stronger noncovalent intermolecular binding needs to be overcome. Compounds capable of intermolecular hydrogen bonding tend to have higher boiling points than those without this capability.

6.2 Distillation Behavior of a Single Volatile Liquid

Figure 6.1 shows the distillation behavior (temperature of distillate, T_{head}, *vs.* volume of the distillate) of a reasonably pure liquid.

Figure 6.1(a) shows the theoretical behavior. From beginning to end, the temperature does not change, and the intercept with the y-axis is the liquid's boiling point. A constant boiling point is one sign of a pure liquid.

Figure 6.1(b) shows what is observed in practice. At the beginning, there is a small amount of liquid with lower boiling point – this is called the **forerun**. Once the thermal equilibrium is reached, the temperature of the distillate (that is, the temperature measured on the thermometer head, T_{head}) remains relatively constant. In the segment shown with level boiling point, a small fluctuation (~1-3 $^{\circ}$C) or rise (up to 5 $^{\circ}$C) might be observed. Deviations this small are not considered significant, and the liquid may still be considered pure. At the end, a significant temperature drop is usually observed. This is the sign that the bulk of the pure liquid has been removed.

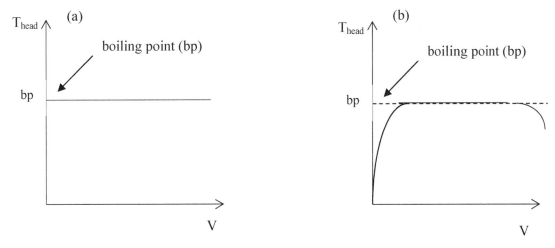

Figure 6.1 Temperature of distillate (T_{head}) *vs.* volume of the distillate for a pure liquid.

6.3 Simple Distillation

Even though simple distillation does not effectively separate a mixture of liquids whose boiling points differ by less than 50 °C, it is commonly used in the following situations in organic laboratory: 1) to obtain a pure liquid product in the last step of a purification and determine the liquid's boiling point; 2) to separate a low-boiling liquid from high-boiling impurities.

In CHE 327, the simple distillation technique is used in Experiment 1, *Simple Distillation*, and Experiment 7, *Synthesis of a Fragrant Ester*.

In the *Ester* experiment, distillation is used as a purification method. In order for the method to succeed, the impurities must boil significantly differently from the desired liquid. In a distillation, an observed boiling point that is essentially constant with only minor fluctuations is a sign of a pure liquid. If two liquids separate well in a distillation, you should observe that each one boils off at its own characteristic constant boiling point. Such behavior indicates that the liquids are pure. If the separation is less efficient, you may observe a gradual rise in temperature (denoting a mixture) and perhaps a leveling off (denoting removal of one component and distillation of the pure remainder).

With the setup shown in Figure 6.2, you can perform a simple distillation that can separate liquids with boiling points differing by at least 50 °C. The distillation apparatus will be adequate to purify your ester, if you have done the prior workup properly. When you distil your ester product, discard the forerun and any fraction that boils at a significantly different temperature from the level-boiling one, but do not be in a hurry to discard anything; be sure you have your product first!

Setting up the Distillation

- **The distilling flask should be at least one-third but no more than one-half full when the distillation starts**. You need to leave room for the expansion of the liquid as it heats up to avoid the liquid bumping over. But on the other hand, you do not want the flask to be so large that most or all of the liquid will become vapor before distilling over into the receiving flask.

- **Grease the ground-glass joints lightly** to prevent them from sticking.

- Support and secure the whole setup. **Cooling water flows in at the bottom and out at the top** of the micro distillation apparatus.

- **Position the thermometer carefully**. Because a liquid tends to get superheated in the process of boiling, the boiling point should be measured above the surface, at the liquid-vapor interface (the **vapor head**). Therefore, the top of the thermometer bulb should be level with the bottom of the side arm of the micro distillation apparatus (see the dotted line in Figure 6.2). This is where the vapor head will be during distillation. Be sure the bulb is entirely immersed in the vapor head but no lower. If the bulb is too low, it will be in contact with superheated vapor, and the boiling point will appear too high. If the bulb is too high, the boiling point will appear too low. Both problems are particularly troublesome with high-boiling liquids. Also, make sure the thermometer bulb is not touching the side of the micro distillation apparatus. Contact with the glass will also result in inaccurate boiling point measurements. Resting the top of the thermometer on a clamp is suggested, where adjusting the height of the clamp is used to adjust the position of the thermometer bulb inside the apparatus.

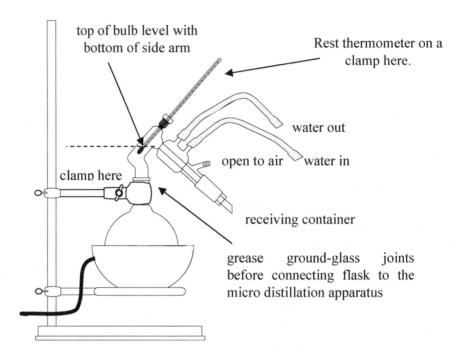

Figure 6.2 A simple distillation setup using the micro distillation apparatus.

- **Add a boiling stone**. This is a porous, inert chip in which small vapor bubbles can form, instead of having a big bubble pop out and perhaps cause the liquid to splash out of the container. This problem is called **bumping**. If you forget the boiling stone and begin heating, let the solution cool a little before adding one. Adding a boiling stone to a superheated solution could cause violent bumping. Because the pores of boiling stones get filled with solvent, every time you let the solution cool and want to reheat it, you should add another stone.

- Plug the heating mantle into the variable transformer (Variac).

Carrying out the Distillation

- Adjust the Variac so that **the dripping rate is about one drop per second**, which indicates that the liquid is boiling and condensing at equilibrium. If you are heating the liquid too intensely, it will flood over. If you are not supplying enough heat to the liquid, it will reflux, and only a few drops will distill occasionally. Either extreme tells you that the system is not at equilibrium; the boiling point you measure may be too high in the first case and too low in the second.

- Record the temperature whenever you change receiving containers, but also periodically when you are collecting a large volume at (relatively) constant temperature. If you observe fluctuations, record these also.

- If you are distilling a compound whose literature boiling point is known, for example your ester, have a realistic idea of how close you can expect the observed boiling point to correspond. Remember to allow for thermometer error, $\pm 5\,^{\circ}C$ at moderate temperatures (below $150\,^{\circ}C$), and $\pm 7\,^{\circ}C$ above.

- For a small sample, as in the *Ester* experiment, there are additional factors that may keep the observed boiling point lower than the literature value – see the experimental write-up. Do not discard any constant-boiling fraction. It is probably reasonably pure, and if it is the main cut, it is probably your ester.

- Discard the forerun. However, do not do so until you are sure you have the greatest amount recoverable of the product. Not being sure where to cut, a novice often keeps more product than necessary in with the forerun. It is better to cut twice, and then later discard the second fraction if necessary. If you cut too late and have a **considerable** amount of product in with the forerun, the only way to recover it is to redistill. (But redistillation has its drawbacks, including loss of material and consumption of time. You may decide not to take this option.)

- If you do not observe a forerun, discard the first few drops anyway. It is better to sacrifice a little product to remove the small amount of impurity that, even if unobserved, is likely to be present.

- Make cuts each time the temperature rises by approximately $5\,^{\circ}C$. The change in temperature is a signal that the composition is changing. But try to limit the number of cuts. The more receivers you use, the more material will be lost on the interior surface of the glassware. Use your own judgment here!

- After you have obtained most of the product, the temperature will rise, signaling that a higher-boiling material is distilling; or it will fall, signaling that there is not enough material distilling to bathe the thermometer bulb. **In either case, stop heating by lowering the mantle immediately.** In the second case, there is the hazard that the pot will dry and get extremely hot; the residue could possibly ignite or explode.

More tips for apparatus setup and use are given in the *Simple Distillation* and *Ester* experiments.

> ### *Safety Precautions*
> - Never plug the heating mantle into the wall socket.
> - Never add a boiling stone to a superheated solution – this could cause violent bumping.
> - Never distill to dryness.

6.4 Fractional Distillation

Fractional distillation will not only separate the liquids, each will emerge pure. Figure 6.3 shows the typical behavior of a successful fractional distillation of a mixture of two liquids.

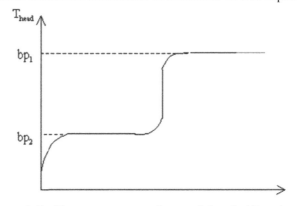

Figure 6.3 Temperature of distillate (T_{head}) *vs.* volume of the distillate in a fractional distillation.

The forerun and the first cut behave as they did in the above description of simple distillation. However, when all the low-boiling liquid has been removed, the temperature jumps suddenly to level off at the boiling point of the second liquid. If care is taken, both liquids can be collected in separate flasks, and the forerun, intermediate fraction, and residue discarded.

If the boiling points are extremely different, the process of fractional distillation can be carried out in the same apparatus as the one you are familiar with. If they are closer, you must use an apparatus that has a greater interior surface area on which vapor can condense and from which liquid can evaporate.

If you know or suspect that there are several liquids with relatively close boiling points in a mixture, you should use a more complicated apparatus designed to accomplish the fractional distillation.

Chapter 7   CRYSTALLIZATION

Crystallization is a common method of purifying organic solids **that contain a small amount of impurities**. The technique of crystallization takes advantage of the greater solubility of a compound in a hot solvent. A saturated solution at a higher temperature normally contains more solute than the same solute-solvent mixture at a lower temperature. Therefore, when the hot saturated solution cools, the solute crystallizes out of the solution.

The crystallization begins with the preparation of a hot saturated solution by dissolving an impure solid (or crystal) in the minimum amount of a hot solvent. *Insoluble* impurities, if any, should be removed at this stage. Then the solution is allowed to cool; crystals of the pure solid form at this stage, leaving *soluble* impurities behind in the supernatant (the solution on the top).

The formation of crystals is a slow process. As the hot saturated solution cools, microcrystals of the solid begin to form. Other molecules of the same substance diffuse to these sites and are incorporated into a regular crystal lattice. Different substances (that is, the impurities) have different molecular geometries and do not fit into the lattice. Thus, the impurities diffuse back into solution and do not become part of the bulk pure crystalline material. If you disturb the crystallizing solution, the process is speeded up; and if there is not time for the impurities to diffuse away, they can become trapped in the lattice by the next wave of molecules building up the crystal. The fast formation of a solid from a saturated solution is called **precipitation**, resulting in smaller and less pure solid. Therefore, slow cooling of the saturated solution gives better (purer) crystals. In some situations, where the solid is wanted quickly and purity is not a major concern, you may try certain methods leading to precipitation.

There will always be some loss of solid in the supernatant because after the crystals form, the solution is saturated at the cold point. However, this loss can be minimized by using no more than the minimum amount of solvent necessary to make a saturated solution at the boiling point.

7.1 Choice of Solvent

The most crucial aspect of a crystallization is the choice of solvent. A proper crystallization solvent is one in which the solid compound has a maximum solubility (very soluble) when it is hot and a minimum solubility (insoluble) when it is cold. Table 7.1 lists some common crystallization solvents.

Table 7.1 Common crystallization solvents (arranged in order of increasing polarity).

Solvent	Formula	Boiling Point ($^\circ$C)	Comment
Ligroin	C_nH_{2n+2}	varies (check the label)	Flammable
Hexanes	C_6H_{14}	67-69	Flammable
Diethyl ether (ether)	$(CH_3CH_2)_2O$	35	Flammable
Ethyl acetate	$CH_3COOCH_2CH_3$	77	Flammable
Methylene chloride (dichloromethane)	CH_2Cl_2	40	Toxic
Acetone	$(CH_3)_2C=O$	56	Flammable
Ethanol (95%)	CH_3CH_2OH	78	Flammable
Methanol	CH_3OH	65	Flammable, toxic
Water	H_2O	100	--------

By the principle "**like dissolves like**", you can sometimes make a useful prediction based on the polarities of the compounds and the solvents. For example, sucrose (table sugar), a polar compound that contains many -OH groups, dissolves in water, a polar solvent. However, you still must determine empirically how soluble the compound is and whether it can be recovered upon cooling. Finding a useful solvent is a process of systematic trial-and-error.

If you find, by the method described below in section 7.2, several solvents that appear suitable, you might be better off using one with a moderate boiling point (65-95 °C). If the boiling point is too low, you will have difficulty controlling evaporation during the heating step. If the boiling point is too high, you cannot boil the solution on the steam bath, which is by far the safest and most convenient way of heating.

7.2 Finding a Proper Crystallization Solvent

Ideally, a solid to be crystallized should be soluble in a solvent when it is hot (usually boiling) and insoluble in the same solvent when it is cold. In the trial-and-error process of finding a solvent, the idea is to test a small amount of the *pure* solid in a variety of solvents, both non-polar and polar. Two questions need to be answered: 1) Is the solid soluble in the not (boiling) solvent? and 2) is it insoluble in the cold solvent? If the answer is yes to both of these, the solvent is likely to be useful for crystallization.

Crystallization, as mentioned above, is a slow process and requires patience. Solvent trials, however, can be done quickly. Here are the steps:

1. Take a small amount (usually 20-30 mg) of the solid to be crystallized and place it in a test tube.

2. Add approximately 1 mL of a trial solvent. Stopper the tube and shake to mix. If the solid dissolves at room temperature, it is soluble. The solute is actually too soluble in this solvent for a crystallization to be effective. This solvent is **not** a proper crystallization solvent.

3. If none (or very little) of the solid dissolves at room temperature, unstopper the tube and carefully heat the mixture (do not forget to add a boiling stone or stick) to boiling.

    a. If the solid still does not dissolve, then it is too insoluble to be used for crystallization. This solvent is also **not** a proper crystallization solvent.

    b. If the solid does dissolve completely in a hot solvent, plunge the solution into an ice-water bath. The formation of solid suggests that this is a good crystallization solvent. (Of course this solid would be a precipitate, not a crystal, but your purpose here is finding the solvent, not doing a careful crystallization.) If the solid does not form, then this solvent is **not** a proper crystallization solvent.

Finding a Crystallization Solvent for a Known Compound

For a known solid compound, since the molecular structure is known and its solubility in a solvent can be predicted following the "like dissolves like" principle, it is relatively easy to narrow down the list of possible crystallization solvents. The crystallization solvent, however, should be tested by the procedure described above.

Experiment 2, *Crystallization of Benzoic Acid*, is an example of crystallization of a known solid. In the solvent trial (Part A), three solvents are tried (the non-polar petroleum ether, the polar ethanol and water) to demonstrate the general procedure. Here are some points to remember:

*   Because you are working with small amounts of material, it is especially important to have your glassware clean and dry. A little acetone or water could affect your observations.

*   Because this is the first time you have done solvent trials, measure three 50-mg portions of benzoic acid, transfer to three small test tubes, and add 1 mL of a different solvent to each. It is important that the amounts of both solid and solvent in all trials be comparable. When you are more experienced, you will not have to measure amounts exactly to achieve this result. For estimating volume, it is convenient to remember that a small test tube holds 3 mL.

Finding a Crystallization Solvent for an Unknown Compound

When the solid to be crystallized is unknown, it is much more difficult to find a crystallization solvent. A wide range of solvents, from non-polar to moderately polar to polar, should be tested.

Here are some modifications that you may need to try:

- Solubility is a relative term. If a solid appears too insoluble in a solvent both hot and cold, you can sometimes increase its solubility to a useful extent by adding more solvent. Conversely, if too soluble, you can repeat a trial with the same amount of solvent but more solid.

- Sometimes you cannot find an individual solvent that has the desired properties. Instead, you find solvents in which the solid is insoluble at all temperatures and in reasonable amounts, and other solvents in which it is too soluble. You can deduce that a mixture of two solvents with the opposite properties might work very well, and indeed there is a very convenient method using what is called a **solvent pair** (see section 7.5).

7.3 General Crystallization Procedure

A general procedure for crystallizing a solid is given below. This is also the procedure used in the *Crystallization* experiment.

Choosing the Solvent

You must test to find a solvent in which the solid is soluble hot and relatively insoluble cold. The method is described in section 7.2. The right degree of solubility is one important factor that ensures the crystallization will work.

Sometimes a suitable solvent can be found in a literature reference, and you can skip this step.

Dissolving the Solid

Work at the steam bath (or at a hot plate if water is used as the solvent). To the solid in an Erlenmeyer flask or a large test tube, add solvent (you may either preheat the solvent or heat it as you add it to the solution) a little at a time, and swirl or tap to mix. When heating a solution, do not forget to add a boiling aid (a stone or a stick).

There are two important factors at this stage, the amount and the temperature of the solvent. You are trying to create a saturated solution. This means you want to add as little solvent as will dissolve all the solid. You must keep the solution boiling, or else you will end up adding more solvent than the necessary minimum. Squirt in a pipetful of solvent, swirl over the steam hole until the solution re-boils, and observe whether undissolved solid remains before repeating this sequence. You should add portions of solvent quickly enough that it does not evaporate faster than you are adding it.

When almost the entire solid has dissolved, carefully examine the solution and the bottom of the container for insoluble impurities – the materials that will not dissolve even with more solvent. You usually will not know about these impurities until you actually observe their presence during solvent addition. Stop adding solvent at this point and remove the insoluble impurities before proceeding. It is easy to mistake insoluble impurities for the solid you wish to crystallize. If you notice that the amount of undissolved material remains the same after adding additional solvent, then that undissolved material is most likely insoluble impurities. If too much solvent has been added as a result of this process, you can always adjust the solvent level by boiling off the excess solvent (and adding more if you overshoot saturation).

If the entire solid has dissolved completely and the solution is not contaminated with intensely colored impurities, simply stop adding solvent, skip the next step and directly go to the cooling step.

Removing the Colored and/or Insoluble Impurities

If the solution has an intense color, **activated charcoal** (or **decolorizing charcoal**) such as Norit, may be needed. Activated charcoal has a large surface area and adsorbs organic compounds, especially colored high molecular weight compounds. Only a small amount should be used because the charcoal particles can adsorb the desired compound as well as colored impurities.

The charcoal and other insoluble impurities, if any, should be removed by **hot filtration** (it is actually a gravity filtration with heating). The setup is shown in Figure 7.1. It consists of a beaker containing a few milliliters of solvent and a boiling stone; on top is a stemless funnel with fluted filter paper (the preparation of fluted filter paper is shown in Figure 7.2); a watch glass lid is optional. A stemless funnel is chosen because it doesn't have a narrow passageway to be clogged by crystals forming from the extra glass surface. Fluted filter paper has a large surface area and spaces for vapors to escape, so that filtration is speeded up. The refluxing solvent in the beaker will heat the glassware so that the solid does not precipitate out while you are trying to filter the solution. Another precaution is to dilute the hot solution a little before filtering. Otherwise, even a minute amount of evaporation could cause precipitation.

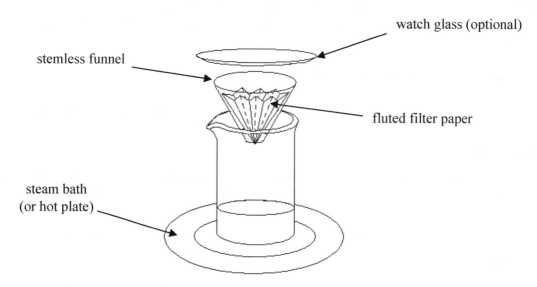

Figure 7.1 Hot filtration setup.

Sometimes, in spite of your care, you may experience some crystal formation in the filter paper. If this is considerable and you do not attempt to recover the material, your final yield will be low. Wash the crystals through with hot solvent, and if the amount you use is more than a few milliliters, you should then evaporate the excess away. As described here, one convenient aspect of the crystallization technique is that you can adjust the degree of saturation by adding and evaporating solvent as needed.

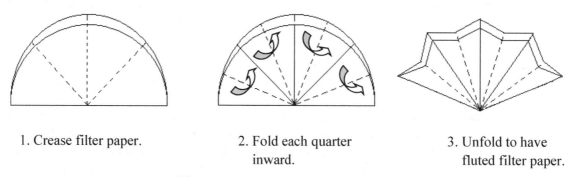

1. Crease filter paper. 2. Fold each quarter inward. 3. Unfold to have fluted filter paper.

Figure 7.2 Preparation of fluted filter paper.

Cooling the Solution

Take the container away, as gently as possible, from the heat source, and let the solution cool slowly to room temperature and then ice temperature. It is recommended that you place the container on a warm surface, such as a book. Your lab bench is a cold surface, and placing the container directly on your lab bench will speed up the cooling process, resulting in smaller, less pure crystals.

Collecting the Crystals

Crystals are usually collected by **vacuum filtration**, which is a technique that quickly and efficiently separates solid from supernatant liquid (gravity filtration works too, but it is much slower). Vacuum filtration is generally used when you want to save the solid rather than the liquid because the liquid might evaporate under vacuum.

The vacuum filtration apparatus is shown in Figure 7.3. It consists of the filtration flask and a trap to prevent backflow from the water aspirator into the filtration flask.

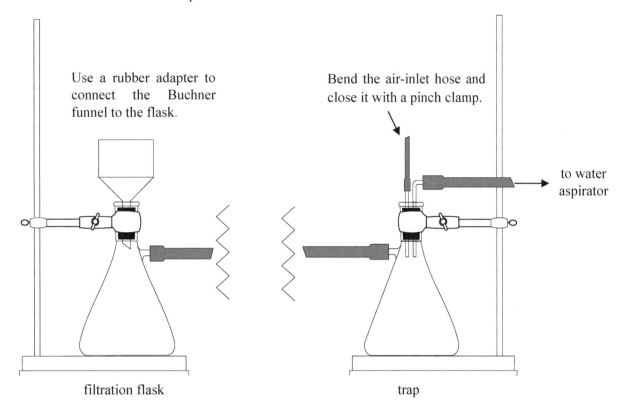

Use a rubber adapter to connect the Buchner funnel to the flask.

Bend the air-inlet hose and close it with a pinch clamp.

to water aspirator

filtration flask

trap

Figure 7.3 A vacuum filtration apparatus (note: the tubing is thick-walled).

Thick-walled vacuum tubing must be used for vacuum connection because ordinary tubing collapses when vacuum is applied. Both flasks should be clamped firmly. It is poor judgment to skip clamping to save time. Contrast the few minutes saved to the hours – and material – lost if a flask tips over.

Choose a piece of filter paper that covers the entire bed of the Buchner funnel without folding up on the sides. If you are using water or ethanol, you might pre-wet the filter paper; skip this step when the solvent is more volatile since it would evaporate too quickly to be of use as a wetting agent. Pour the mixture of crystals and liquid into the funnel to wet the paper, taking care that the paper does not float up. Then turn on the aspirator water and close the pinch clamp of the trap. If you have a vacuum, the liquid will flow through quite quickly.

If you need to hold the funnel down to get a good vacuum, do this with both hands grasping the sides. Do not put your palm on the top – dry solid could go flying when you break the vacuum by removing your hand.

You should suck all the liquid through until the solid appears dry (it will not actually be completely dry yet). Most vacuum filtrations are followed by a wash step.

Remember to allow the air to enter the filtration system by opening the pinch clamp before turning off the aspirator water. Otherwise, you may expect water backup into the trap flask.

Washing the Crystals

This step washes away the supernatant, which contains impurities; if the supernatant is simply left to evaporate, these impurities would be deposited on the surface of the crystals. To wash the crystals, open the pinch clamp first to release the vacuum. Then add enough of the solvent used for crystallization to cover the entire collected crystals (the solvent should be ice-cold).

Drying the Crystals

There are different methods of drying crystals. The simplest one is air-drying, in which the crystals are spread on a watch glass or a large piece of filter paper. Air-drying may be slow, especially when water or another high-boiling solvent was used. Usually you have to wait a few days for water to evaporate off completely. On the other hand, if the solvent is volatile, like ether or ligroin, drying can take place in less than an hour.

There are several times in CHE 327 where this plan is suggested. Here are a few hints to help you accomplish air-drying:

- Spread the solid out to expose a large surface area. Store the solid in your drawer in a container that has a large opening.

- Be sure the storage container is stable and has reasonably high sides. A beaker is good. A weighing dish or watch glass is not. Remember, when the solid is dry, it will be lightweight, and just opening your drawer may cause it to be blown around.

- Try not to scrape a wet solid off of filter paper because otherwise you might also scrape off fibers of the paper. Once the solid is dry, it can be transferred without this problem.

- If you need to dry a small amount of solid in a hurry, sometimes you can do so by pressing it between pieces of filter paper, chopping it with your spatula, and spreading it out on the filter paper to expose it to the air.

- Some materials are unstable to air or moisture or they sublime. These materials should not be air-dried.

Second Crop Crystals

A second crop of crystals can sometimes be obtained by evaporating some of the solvent from the filtrate (the liquid collected in the filter flask) and cooling the solution again. The second crop crystals usually are not as pure as the first crop. Therefore, the two crops should not be combined unless the purities (usually indicated by both appearance and melting point) are proved to be comparable.

Safety Precautions

- Most organic solvents used for crystallizations are volatile and flammable. Therefore, they should be heated on a steam bath or in a hot water bath, not on a hot plate.

- Never use a hot plate near flammable solvents.

- Never add a boiling stone to a superheated solution – it could cause violent bumping.

- Hold a hot Erlenmeyer flask with a clamp. Do not use a test tube holder – it is not designed to hold an Erlenmeyer flask securely.

7.4 Small-Scale Crystallization

When the amount of the solid to be crystallized is small (usually < 300 mg), a slightly different version of the crystallization technique is necessary. In Experiment 8, *Multi-Step Synthesis of Lidocaine*, small-scale crystallization is used to purify the crude produce made from the first step of the synthesis. Even though many steps are the same, the technique appears different because you are working with a much smaller amount of material and different types of smaller containers need to be used.

Here are the steps of the small-scale crystallization:

1. Find a suitable crystallization solvent (or solvent pair) as described above in section 7.2. In Experiment 8, the solvent choice is determined for you.

2. Dissolve the solid in a test tube (or other small-scale container). A test tube rather than an Erlenmeyer flask has been chosen because the size of the glassware should be suited to the amount of solution. In any operation, if you use glassware that is too large, you will lose material unnecessarily over its interior surface.

   Try to use the minimum amount of hot solvent because less product will be recovered from a solution that is not saturated.

3. Cool the solution undisturbed to room temperature and then ice temperature. Cooling a small amount of solution will probably take no more than 10 minutes. Such cooling periods are convenient for doing other lab work; in this experiment it is suggested that you prepare your wash solvent at this time.

4. Remove the supernatant using an unchipped pipet: squeeze the air out of the bulb and carefully press the tip of the pipet flat to the bottom of the test tube; slowly release the bulb to remove the supernatant solution by drawing it up into the pipet, keeping the solid in the test tube. Then wash with a small amount of cold solvent. Remove as much supernatant as possible before washing. Divide your wash solvent into several portions, and mix each one well with the solid before you pipet it out. Keep everything cold throughout; and if you see an alarming decrease in the amount of product, do not perform additional washes.

7.5 Crystallization from a Solvent Pair (Mixed Solvent)

When no single solvent appears suitable for crystallization, a solvent pair may be used. A solvent pair consists of two miscible solvents: one dissolves the solid readily and another does not. Although using a solvent pair is a bit more complicated than using a single solvent, it has the advantage of your being able to tailor-make solubility.

Here are the steps:

1. In your trials, identify the two solvents, one in which the solid is too soluble (we call it the good solvent) and the other in which it is too insoluble (the poor solvent). Of course, the two solvents must be miscible.

2. Depending on the scale of the crystallization, put the solid in either an Erlenmeyer or large test tube.

3. Just barely cover the solid with the good solvent. Add a boiling aid, and heat. If the solid all dissolves, do not add more. If it does not, add this good solvent in small portions just as in a conventional crystallization until complete solubility is achieved. (If a hot filtration needs to be done, it should be done now.)

4. Keeping everything boiling, add the poor solvent dropwise while swirling gently until the solution turns cloudy or a precipitate forms, indicating that you have just overshot the saturation point. Stop adding the poor solvent.

5. Now, keeping everything boiling, add more of the good solvent dropwise until the cloudiness just disappears – you have corrected the situation back to the saturation point. Then add a few more drops to ensure an excess of the good solvent.

6. Remove the container from the steam bath and let the solution cool. Continue as usual.

7.6 Crystallization from Water

Water has a high boiling point, which makes it a relatively inconvenient crystallization solvent. Solids crystallized from water require a considerably longer drying period than from other solvents.

Water, however, is very useful in a solvent pair with ethanol or methanol. And in certain cases, it is the best single solvent for a particular crystallization. If you choose water, set the hot plate up in the fume hood, away from flammable solvents. Allow enough time for your bulk crystals to dry; and you might want to use the quick-dry technique of pressing a small amount of the crystals between filter paper.

Chapter 8   MELTING POINT

The **melting point** of a solid is the temperature at which transition from solid to liquid occurs at one atmospheric pressure. However, unlike the effect on boiling point, the effect of a small change in the pressure on melting point is negligible and usually ignored.

Each pure compound has its own characteristic melting point. In theory, this value could be measured accurately and reported in the literature. In practice, the measurement is not so accurate; you will often run across slightly different melting point reports for the same compound in different literature sources.

The melting point is determined by heating a very small amount of the solid slowly (ideally at the rate of about 1 $^{\circ}$C per minute). Although we use the term melting **point**, what you will actually measure in most cases is a **range**; that is, the beginning (first appearance of liquid) and end (last disappearance of solid) are not at the same temperature. For instance, a typical melting point range for trimyristin might be observed 53-54 $^{\circ}$C. (Note that the term "range" is also used to mean the difference between the high and low value. When the two meanings become confusing, it is convenient to talk about the **span** of the range, in this example, 1 $^{\circ}$C.)

8.1 Characteristics of Melting Point

As mentioned earlier, each pure compound has its characteristic melting point. Two key words here are pure and characteristic. **You can use the melting point measurement to get information about the purity and identity of a compound.**

A pure organic solid often has a sharp melting point and melts over a range of 1.0 $^{\circ}$C or less, while a less pure solid exhibits a broad melting range. Usually, a melting range of 2 $^{\circ}$C or less indicates a pure compound.

An impure compound also exhibits a lower (**depressed**) melting point compared to that of the pure solid. For example, purified trimyristin might melt at 53-54 $^{\circ}$C, but crude trimyristin might have a melting point of 48-52 $^{\circ}$C.

Melting point information can also be used to identify an unknown solid. There are many reference books and literature papers containing lists of compounds with their melting points. It is not possible to identify an unknown compound without more specific information because there are hundreds of compounds with the same melting point. However, you can determine whether two samples with the same melting point are the same by taking a **mixed melting point**, which will be discussed in section 8.4 in more detail.

8.2 Melting-Point Apparatus

Several different types of electrically heated melting point devices are commercially available, for example, the Barnstead Electrothermal Mel-Temp (Figure 8.1) and the Fisher-Johns hot stage apparatus, as well as the Thomas-Hoover melting point apparatus (Figure 8.2).

The Barnstead Electrothermal Digital Mel-Temp shown in Figure 8.1 is a popular melting point apparatus model. The digital system features a built-in temperature display, microprocessor-controlled temperature ramping, and rapid fan cooling. Temperature is sensed by a platinum RTD (Resistance Temperature Detector). During a melting point measurement, the on-set (or "start") temperature and the off-set (or "end") temperature can be recorded and read from the digital display.

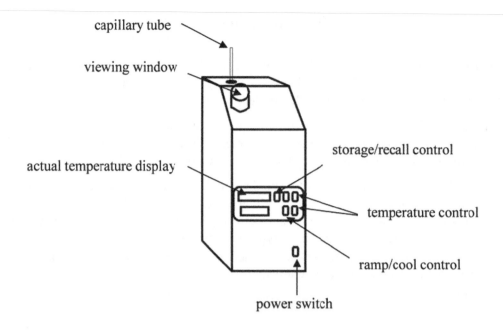

Figure 8.1 The Barnstead Mel-Temp 3.0 melting-point apparatus.

The Thomas-Hoover melting point apparatus shown in Figure 8.2 is also used in our laboratory. In this instrument, capillary tubes containing solid sample are submerged in an electrically heated oil bath. A magnifying glass is used to view the crystals in the capillary tubes clearly. In some more advanced versions of Thomas-Hoover melting point apparatus, a periscope is also provided so that the mercury (or dyed alcohol) thread of the thermometer and the crystals in the capillary tubes can be viewed simultaneously.

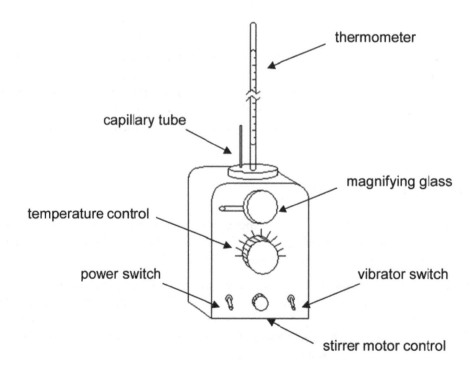

Figure 8.2 The Thomas-Hoover melting-point apparatus.

8.3 Determining Melting Point

Preparing the Sample

Determination of a melting point is an analytical technique. This means that you need only an extremely small sample to make the measurement. The amount of sample that goes into the melting point tube (or capillary tube) should be of approximately the same height as the width of the tube (~ 1-2 mm) – you will see that this is on the order of a few milligrams.

Figure 8.3 illustrates how to load a melting point tube. Crush a few milligrams of the dry solid into a fine powder, and mix to get a uniform sample. Press the open end of the melting point tube into the mound of powder to make a small plug, as shown in Figure 8.3. Invert the tube and tap it on the bench top so that the sample packs down at the bottom. Then insert the sample tube into the melting-point instrument. There are five holes for tubes, but it is impractical to try to take five melting points at a time. However, you should take two or three at a time whenever you are comparing values (for example the crude and purified trimyristin).

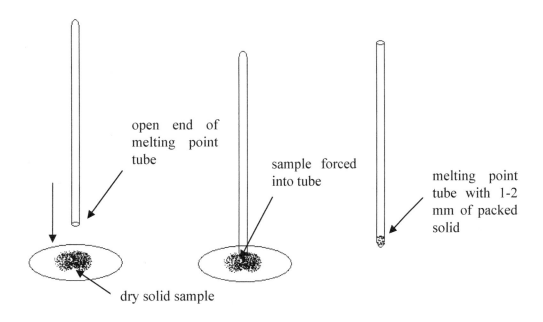

open end of melting point tube

sample forced into tube

melting point tube with 1-2 mm of packed solid

dry solid sample

Figure 8.3 Loading a melting point tube.

Heating the Sample to its Melting Point

Turn on the power/light switch; adjust the stirrer for gentle action.

Turn the heat-select knob to raise the temperature quickly to about 10-15 $^{\circ}$C below the expected melting point of the sample. Then adjust the knob so that the temperature is rising no more than 1-2 $^{\circ}$C /minute. If you are impatient at this step, you may get an artificially high melting point and/or broad range.

If the melting point of the sample is unknown, it will save time to take a preliminary melting point first by rapidly heating. (Of course this preliminary melting point will be inaccurate, but it will give you an idea at what temperature, approximately, the sample will melt.) Then take a careful measurement of a second sample. Decomposition at the melting temperature is common, giving rise to impurities. For this reason, you should always prepare a fresh sample for each melting point measurement.

Recording the Melting Point

Record the appearance of the first drop of liquid and the disappearance of the last piece of solid – this is the melting point range. Be sure to record values directly into your notebook, both the beginning and end of melting. Look carefully for the first drop of liquid – shrinking or movement of solid does not count.

An example of the proper way for a student to report an observed melting point range: Melting point (or MP, mp) of crystallized benzoic acid = 121-123 $^{\circ}$C. If you are discussing purity, it is often appropriate to cite the span of the range, which is 2 $^{\circ}$C in the above example. If your solid happens to melt at one temperature, it should still be recorded with two values. For example, benzoic acid = 121-123 $^{\circ}$C.

Interpreting the Melting Point

If a compound is pure, its melting point value will be close to the one in the literature, and the range will be sharp.

How close to the literature value should the melting point be? Because thermometers are usually not calibrated, there is an unknown source of error in any melting point measurement. This error could occur in the literature, in your value, or neither or both. You should allow ±5 $^{\circ}$C as a margin of error (from the offset temperature) at low MP temperatures, and slightly more (about ±7 $^{\circ}$C) at higher temperatures (greater than 150 $^{\circ}$C).

How sharp should the range be? The sharper the better, although for many purposes as much as 2 $^{\circ}$C is acceptable. If the compound is impure, its melting point value will be **depressed**, or its range will be **broadened**, or both.

Some Situations You Might Encounter in CHE 327 and Their Interpretation

- Your "pure" trimyristin has a melting point of 53.5-54 $^{\circ}$C. The literature value is 56 $^{\circ}$C.

  Interpretation: The 2 $^{\circ}$C difference of the offset temperature from the literature value is insignificant, and the range is 0.5 $^{\circ}$C. The product is indeed pure.

- Your "pure" trimyristin has a melting point of 50-54 $^{\circ}$C.

  Interpretation: Although there is the same 2 $^{\circ}$C difference from the literature value, the range is 4 $^{\circ}$C, and the product is impure. (But if you take your measurement too quickly, you might observe this same result. It is worth a check.)

- Your "pure" trimyristin has a melting point of 52-54 $^{\circ}$C.

  Interpretation: It is pure enough for most purposes.

- You have an unknown whose melting point you have measured at 112-113 $^{\circ}$C.

  Interpretation: The 1 $^{\circ}$C range tells you the compound is pure. Therefore, you can have reasonable confidence that the literature value lies ±5 $^{\circ}$C from your measurement, that is, between 107 $^{\circ}$C and 118 $^{\circ}$C. This information will be very useful in identifying the compound.

8.4 Mixed Melting Point

From the following description of the technique, you will see why some purists prefer the more accurately descriptive term, "mixture melting point."

Because there are literally millions of organic solids, a large number of them happen to have the same literature melting point. In fact, trimyristin and myristic acid, the products from Experiment 3, *Trimyristin from Nutmeg*, and Experiment 4, *Myristic Acid from Trimyristin*, exemplify this situation.

Their literature values are 56 $^{\circ}$C and 54 $^{\circ}$C respectively; and because of the ± 5 $^{\circ}$C allowance for error, these are experimentally indistinguishable. Taking a melting point of a white solid obtained at the end of the myristic acid synthesis will not answer the question: "How do you know that the solid is myristic acid rather than unreacted trimyristin?"

A **mixed melting point** is a clever way to answer this question. It relies on the fact that a pure sample melts high and sharp, and an impure sample melts low and/or broad. Thus, even though two different compounds happen to have the same melting point, a mixture of the two of them is impure, and it will behave accordingly.

Here is how to use mixed melting point to distinguish trimyristin from myristic acid:

1. In the usual way, prepare one capillary tube with your purest trimyristin, and another with your purest myristic acid.

2. Take small samples of each of the two compounds, and grind and mix them together well in an approximate 1:1 ratio. Put this mixture in a third tube.

3. Put all three tubes in the instrument together so that you can make the best direct comparison of their melting behavior. The mixture is actually a very impure material, and the typical melting point behavior of an impure solid would be expected.

Chapter 9   EXTRACTION AND DRYING

Extraction is a technique which in its most common application uses a solvent to separate a compound from a mixture. Examples of extraction include:

- Making tea: extracting soluble tea substances into water, leaving behind the leaves

- Isolating trimyristin from nutmeg (in the *Trimyristin* experiment): extracting trimyristin into ether, leaving behind the nutmeg grounds

- Doing laundry: extracting out the dirt, leaving behind the clothes

- Removing unwanted acids that are present in an ether solution of the ester product (in the *Ester* experiment): extracting the acids into base, leaving behind the ester still dissolved in the ether solution

Although there are several different types of extraction methods, **liquid-liquid extraction** (or simply extraction) is the most common one. It involves the distribution of a compound between two immiscible liquids, or **phases**. By taking advantage of different solubilities, compounds can be selectively chosen and therefore transported from one solvent to another.

In the organic laboratory, extraction is often used as part of a purification process. Sometimes the material extracted is desired, as in the first two examples. At other times the material extracted is unwanted, as in the last two examples. When unwanted material is extracted out into a solvent, the process is sometimes called **washing**. In the last example, the mixture containing the ester and acids is washed with base, and the base washes are discarded.

9.1 Extraction Theory

As mentioned above, in an extraction the desired material can be transported from one phase to another. For example, material that is dissolved in water can be extracted into ether. Because water and ether are not miscible, the two layers that form can be physically separated, and the material dissolved in the ether can be isolated from that in the water. Since the material is soluble in both water and ether, why does it move from one of these solvents (at least partially) to the other? This is an equilibrium situation, described by the equation below, in which the constant K has the special name of **partition coefficient**.

$$K = \frac{\text{concentration of compound in solvent 2}}{\text{concentration of compound in solvent 1}}$$

If K is larger than 1, for example if K= 6, then for equal amounts of the two solvents, there will be six times as much of the material dissolved in solvent 2 (in this case ether) as there is in solvent 1 (water). Therefore, most of the material will be extracted from water into ether. And if the extraction is repeated with fresh ether, most of the remaining material will be extracted into this second ether portion. The two ether extracts combined contain essentially all of the material that was originally dissolved in water.

9.2 The Extraction Procedure

General Procedure

Extractions are usually carried out in a **separatory funnel** of proper size, as shown in Figure 9.1. The separatory funnel is a very convenient piece of apparatus that can be a hazard if not used properly.

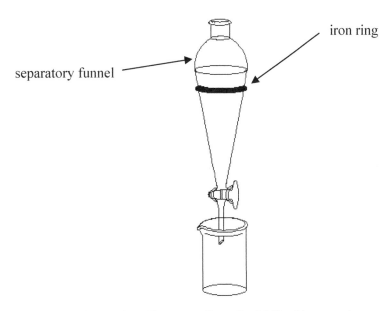

iron ring

separatory funnel

Figure 9.1 The setup for a liquid-liquid extraction.

Here are the steps, with some tips, that should help you avoid problems:

1. Set up the funnel in an iron ring on the ring stand as shown in Figure 9.1. Close the stopcock. Put an empty container underneath the stem in case of leaks. Pour some water in to test for any leaks from the stopcock. Drain the water after the leak test.

2. Pour your mixture into the funnel. The funnel should not be more than about 3/4 full so that you will have room to shake the contents.

3. Stopper the funnel. Take it out of the ring and invert it while holding the stopper closed. Open the stopcock to let out the vapor that is forming and exerting pressure – this is called **venting**.

4. Close the stopcock. Shake the funnel gently once or twice. Vent again. Repeat, shaking a few more times and venting.

5. Put the funnel back in the ring (with the container underneath), and remove the stopper. Allow the two layers to separate. Open the stopcock to drain out the lower layer. Depending on what you are doing experimentally, you might be saving or discarding the layer you remove first.

    When you separate the layers, be sure you know which is which material. A good rule of thumb is to consider the density of each solvent – the denser solvent will be on the bottom (although sometimes the situation is changed by what might be dissolved in either solvent). Densities of some common organic solvents are listed in Table 9.1.

Table 9.1 Common extraction solvents.

Solvent	Formula	Density (g/ml)	Comment
Diethyl ether (ether)	$(CH_3CH_2)_2O$	0.7	Flammable
Hexanes	C_6H_{14}	~0.7	Flammable
Ethyl acetate	$CH_3COOCH_2CH_3$	0.9	Flammable
Water	H_2O	1.0	----
Methylene chloride (dichloromethane)	CH_2Cl_2	1.3	toxic

In cases of doubt, you could add one or two drops of each layer to a test tube of water to see which one the water is miscible with.

When you separate the layers, you also need to know which layer is the one to save and which to discard. Even if you believe you know the answer to this question, it is a very good idea to label all layers and save them until you have progressed far enough in the experiment to be absolutely sure.

Safety Precautions

- You must vent at the beginning.

- Do not point the stem of the separatory funnel toward anyone, including yourself.

Extraction in the Trimyristin Experiment

The solid-liquid extraction technique is used in the *Trimyristin* experiment, in which trimyristin is extracted from ground nutmeg (solid) by ether (liquid) because it is soluble in ether and many of the other substances in nutmeg are not. However, other organic compounds in nutmeg are ether-soluble as well. For this reason, extraction does not produce pure trimyristin, but rather a crude mixture.

Following are some tips that should help you get a good yield of soluble material in this experiment. Note that for this experiment a separatory funnel is not used.

- Mix the ether and nutmeg well by frequent swirling. Stirring might help if the solids lump up, but often it is not necessary and you might just as well avoid the mess. Note that the most convenient way to swirl is by using an Erlenmeyer flask that is not too full (half-full is usually just right).

- Allow enough time for the dissolving to take place.

9.3 Acid-Base Extraction

Consider an ether solution that contains both a neutral and an acidic substance. If you mix this solution with an aqueous base, there will be two layers, one ether and the other aqueous. If you shake the layers together vigorously, the acid can react with base and form a water-soluble salt. The neutral substance will remain in the ether, and the salt will dissolve in the aqueous phase.

$$\text{acid} \quad + \quad \text{base} \quad \rightarrow \quad \text{salt}$$
$$\text{(ether-soluble)} \quad \text{(aqueous)} \quad \text{(water-soluble)}$$

The opposite tactic, extracting a salt formed from a basic substance and an aqueous acid, is also practical. It will be used during Experiment 8, *Multi-Step Synthesis of Lidocaine*.

Acid-Base Extraction in the Ester Experiment

In Experiment 7, *Synthesis of a Fragrant Ester*, the ester product you synthesize is very impure. Because you used twice as much carboxylic acid as alcohol, even in the best case (where all of the alcohol is converted to ester), there will still be as much unreacted carboxylic acid at the end of the reaction as there is product! This unreacted acid must be removed, and acid-base extraction is a convenient way to do it.

Note that you will be using acid-base extraction for washing, that is, removing an unwanted material into the extracting solvent and keeping the original solution which contains the wanted ester product. You will put both the initial water solution and the ether into the funnel and shake these liquids together, then let the mixture settle and separate the layers.

Following are some tips that should help you get a good yield of pure ester in this experiment:

- Before beginning the acid-base extraction, do a simple liquid-liquid extraction with cold water to remove the sulfuric acid catalyst that is still present. If it is not removed here, the sulfuric acid will react strongly with the base in the next step, heating up the ether and making it evaporate. You will have a real mess.

- Keep the ether layer and extract it with 10% aqueous sodium carbonate, a base. The following reaction occurs:

$$2RCOOH + Na_2CO_3 \rightarrow 2\,RCOO^-Na^+ + CO_2\uparrow + H_2O$$

Because this reaction gives carbon dioxide gas as a side product, you run it in an Erlenmeyer flask before transferring the mixture to the separatory funnel. This way, you allow most of the gas to escape before you shake the mixture up in the closed funnel. Even with this precaution, do not forget to vent frequently.

- One extraction will almost certainly not be enough. Keep doing extractions with fresh sodium carbonate until the litmus test (see below) tells you that you have removed all the acid.

- Initially, the aqueous layer is basic. In the first extraction, there is so much acid present in the organic layer, that there is enough to neutralize all the base. After several extractions there will be no more acid in the ether layer, no more neutralization will take place, and the aqueous layer will remain basic. Test the aqueous layer with litmus paper each time so you can determine when no more extractions are needed. Keep in mind that the neutralization reaction may be slow; therefore, be sure to shake well and to allow enough time before doing the litmus test.

- It will not hurt to do perhaps one more extraction than necessary, but do not be overzealous. Generally, avoid doing more transfers than necessary because each transfer causes some loss of material.

- Ether is volatile (boiling point ~ 35 $^\circ$C). Check the layer every so often, and add more ether to maintain approximately the original volume. If the ether solution of ester becomes too concentrated, every time you transfer it you will lose more ester on the glassware surface than if you were transferring a dilute solution.

9.4 Drying Organic Liquids

Most liquid-liquid extractions in an organic laboratory include an organic phase and an **aqueous** (water) phase. The two solvents are generally immiscible. But no two solvents are completely immiscible. As a result, some water is always present in the organic phase no matter how careful you are. Therefore, before removing it from the isolated organic phase to recover the desired compound, the solution should be dried so that contamination from water will be avoided.

Water completely dissolved in an organic solvent is invisible (meaning the solution remains clear) and can usually be removed by a **drying agent**. If its solubility is exceeded, water can cause cloudiness or can separate out as droplets. The visible water cannot be removed by a drying agent and should be separated by a different method. A note on terminology: The word **clear** means **not cloudy**. Do not use it to mean **colorless**, a completely different idea.

Drying Agents

Drying agents are anhydrous inorganic salts that form hydrates in the presence of water. For example, anhydrous sodium sulfate can react with water to form $Na_2SO_4\bullet7H_2O$. You will use two drying agents in CHE 327, sodium sulfate and magnesium sulfate. Both are reasonably fast, effective, and cheap.

Here are the steps for drying organic liquids:

1. Observe whether there is any visible water. The drying agent's capacity (the ability to bind the water) is limited, so get rid of a water layer or drops if at all possible before proceeding.

2. Because the mixture must be swirled, put your solution in an Erlenmeyer flask that will be about half full, no more. A beaker is not a good choice for any operation requiring swirling.

3. Pour enough drying agent into the flask to cover a thin layer at the bottom. Swirl intermittently for several minutes. If you have enough time, allow ten minutes for this step.

4. Observe whether some of the drying agent is free-flowing like sand. The part that has reacted with water will be sticky or lumpy. If there is no sandy phase, you will need to transfer the liquid to a new flask and treat with fresh drying agent. If you do, you may want to rinse the residue in the first flask with a little solvent and add the rinse to the second flask.

5. Remove the drying agent. With sodium sulfate, decanting is a practical method of transferring the supernatant solution. With magnesium sulfate, filtering will probably work better.

Drying in the β-Carotene Experiment

In Experiment 6, *Isolation of β-Carotene from Spinach by Column Chromatography*, the ethyl acetate/pigments solution should be dried with anhydrous sodium sulfate before proceeding.

The ethyl acetate you use to dissolve the plant pigments will also dissolve some water. Rotary evaporation is effective in removing the organic solvent but not the water. If not removed by the drying agent, the water will wet the chromatography adsorbent. When the pigments are analyzed by TLC, the effect of this wetting is a noticeable drag on the pigment spots, causing lower R_f values than would otherwise be observed.

Drying in the Ester Experiment

In Experiment 7, *Synthesis of a Fragrant Ester*, after a series of base extractions, you will have an ether solution of ester. This solution contains water and must be dried before solvent is removed by rotary evaporation and final distillation.

If not removed by the drying agent, the water will distil over along with the ester. Two liquids that are miscible and have very different boiling points can be separated by distillation, but a mixture of immiscible liquids behaves differently. Each distils as if the other were not present. This means that if there are two phases before the distillation, there will be two at the end, and the ester will be contaminated with water.

9.5 Other Techniques Related to Extraction

After an extraction has been completed and the extract (the solution containing the desired compound) dried, the solvent in the extract is usually removed to recover the desired compound. As a matter of fact, in an organic laboratory, there will be many situations where you want to get rid of solvents and will use one of the evaporation techniques discussed below.

A small amount of solvent can be removed by evaporation on a steam bath in a hood or by blowing it off with nitrogen or dry air in a hood. However, boiling away large amounts of solvent into the atmosphere is prohibited by environmental law. Large amounts of solvent should be removed by distillation or rotary evaporation so that the solvent can be collected and perhaps recycled.

The Rotary Evaporator (Rotovap)

The **rotary evaporator** (or "**rotovap**") is a rather complicated piece of equipment designed to remove large amounts of volatile solvent quickly and safely.

The rotovap, as shown in Figure 9.2, is hooked up to a vacuum source (either a water aspirator, 10 in Figure 9.2, or a diaphragm pump), and controlled by a stopcock (8 in Figure 9.2). As you know, under vacuum a liquid boils lower than its normal boiling point. The rotovap allows you to boil solvent away at a moderate temperature. Evaporation also causes cooling. To counteract this, you use a heating bath (4 in Figure 9.2, filled with water or oil) under the round bottom flask containing the solution. Without the bath, the solution would get so cold that ice would form on the outside of the flask, and evaporation would slow dramatically.

The reason the apparatus is rotated is twofold: to spread the liquid over a large surface area for more efficient evaporation; and to provide a swirling motion so that large bubbles do not form and cause the liquid to splash.

Most of the apparatus consists of traps that protect the material you are saving in the round bottom flask. As shown in Figure 9.2, a bumping trap (3 in Figure 9.2) is to catch any liquid that may splash up. So that you can recover this liquid if you need it, the trap should be reasonably clean before you attach your flask. A condenser (9 in Figure 9.2) containing ice (or dry ice) condenses the evaporated solvent, which is then collected in the receiving flask (11 in Figure 9.2) for eventual discard. There may also be a trap connected between the condenser and the vacuum to protect against water backup from the aspirator, which will happen if you turn off the water before you break the vacuum – the water is sucked in. This problem can also occur, through no error of your own, if the aspirator is defective.

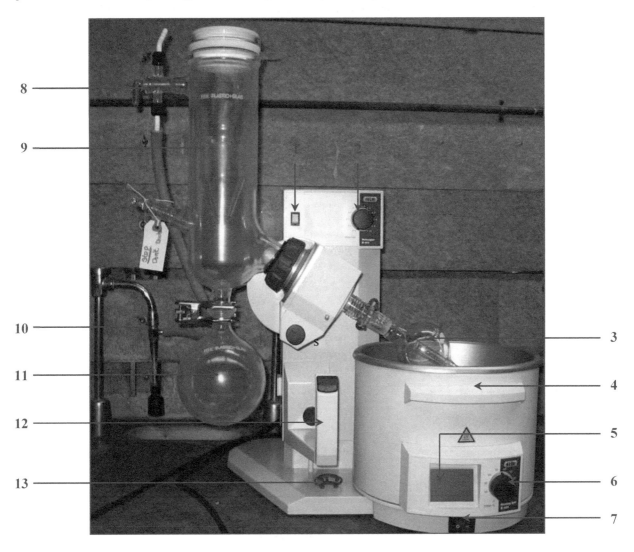

Figure 9.2 Buchi R-210C rotovap.

1. Power switch of rotovap
2. Knob for adjusting rotation speed
3. Bumping trap
4. Heating bath
5. Bath temperature display
6. Knob for adjusting bath temperature
7. Power switch of heating bath
8. Stopcock for vacuum control
9. Condenser
10. Water aspirator
11. Receiving flask
12. Quick-action jack
13. Clip

Follow these steps when you use the rotovap:

1. If a warm water bath is needed, set up the heating bath (4 in Figure 9.2), otherwise skip to step 2. Note that usually the heating bath is already ready for use. In case it is switched off, set it up as following:

   • Fill the heating bath (about half-full) with water.

   • Switch on (7 in Figure 9.2) the heating bath. The set temperature appears in the display. Do not change the setting, which is usually set at the optimal distilling temperature for the solvent you use.

2. Ask your TA to fill the condenser (9 in Figure 9.2) with ice.

3. Check the receiving flask (11 in Figure 9.2). If the flask is more than half-full with liquid from former users, ask your TA to empty it before proceeding.

4. Check vacuum control stopcock (8 in Figure 9.2) and make sure it is open to air ("up" position in the Figure 9.3a).

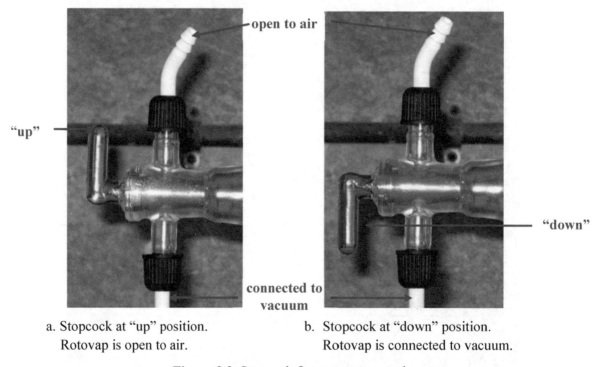

a. Stopcock at "up" position. b. Stopcock at "down" position.
   Rotovap is open to air.   Rotovap is connected to vacuum.

Figure 9.3 Stopcock for vacuum control.

5. Check the main switch of the rotovap (1 in Figure 9.2). It should be left on during the lab. In case the rotovap is switched off by the previous user, switch it on.

6. Attach your flask to the bumping trap (3 in Figure 9.2). Clip (with the plastic clip, 13 in Figure 9.2) the flask in place with caution, keeping your right hand underneath your flask.

7. Check the water aspirator and make sure the water is turned on.

8. Turn vacuum control stopcock (8 in Figure 9.2) to vacuum source ("down" position in Figure 9.3b).

9. Gently push the "▼" sign on the handle of the quick-action jack (12 in Figure 9.2) to lower your flask. Adjust the height of the flask until the level of solution in the flask about equal with the water level in the heating bath.

10. Start the rotation by turning the adjusting knob for rotation speed (2 in Figure 9.2).

11. When you have finished evaporating and are ready to remove your flask, stop the rotation by turning the rotation speed adjusting knob (2 in Figure 9.2) to 0.

12. Raise the flask gently pushing the "▲" sign on the handle of the quick-action jack (12 in Figure 1).

13. Placing your right hand gently underneath your flask, **open the vacuum control stopcock (8 in Figure 9.2) to air ("up" position in Figure 9.3a) so that the vacuum inside the rotovap is broken**.

14. Unclip and remove the flask with caution.

15. You do not need to turn off the pump or the rotovap. Leave them on for the next user. If no other student is waiting in line, you may turn off the water.

Chapter 10   REFLUX

Reflux means boiling a liquid and condensing the vapors back into the same container. The reflux temperature is near the boiling point of the liquid. By this practice, you accomplish two things: 1) maintain a constant temperature – the liquid's boiling point – and 2) keep the liquid from evaporating away while you still need it.

10.1 Typical Reflux Setup

A typical setup of a reflux apparatus is shown in Figure 10.1.

The purpose of the water-cooled condenser is to keep the liquid from evaporating away to any great extent; but you must take care not to apply too much heat. You should check the vapor head, which is the line where the solvent is seen condensing and running back into the flask. The vapor head should be no more than 1/4 the way up the condenser. If it is higher, you must lower the voltage setting on the transformer (Variac in our lab).

The cooling water should do its job if you adjust the heat input properly. Do not try to keep the vapors in by using a stopper.

More details about the apparatus setup and takedown are discussed in the experimental instructions of Experiment 4, *Myristic Acid from Trimyristin*. The same points apply in Experiment 7, *Synthesis of a Fragrant Ester*, and Experiment 8, *Multi-Step Synthesis of Lidocaine*.

> **Safety Precautions**
> Never heat a closed system – it could cause an explosion!

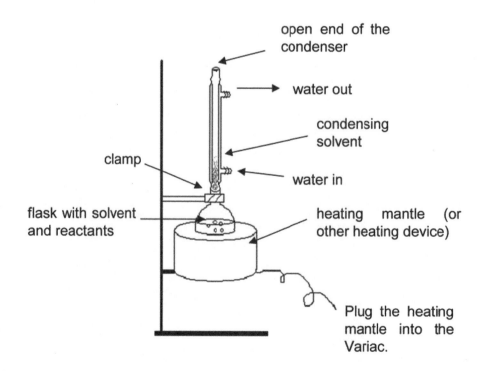

Figure 10.1 A typical reflux setup.

10.2 Variations of the Reflux Apparatus

You do not always need the special setup in Figure 10.1 to have a reflux. You only need the top of the glassware to be colder than the bottom. For example, in the *Trimyristin* experiment, you may have observed the vapor head when you heated the trimyristin solution on the steam bath in the round bottom flask.

When you are heating, sometimes you want to keep liquid in reflux. An Erlenmeyer flask, with a small mouth, is good for this purpose. At other times, to evaporate off liquid, a beaker would be more suitable.

When you have a particular task to accomplish, it is tempting to grab the first clean piece of glassware; but often a wrong choice will cost you more in time than would the extra cleaning step.

Chapter 11   CHROMATOGRAPHY

11.1 Introduction to Chromatography

Chromatography is a versatile and widely used method for identifying and separating compounds in a mixture. It got this name because it was first used to separate mixtures of different colored substances. Today, it can be used to follow the course of a reaction, to separate components of a mixture, and to identify compounds.

All chromatographic methods involve the distribution of the substances between a **stationary phase** and a **mobile (or moving) phase**. The mixture applied to the stationary phase (solid or liquid) is carried through the mobile phase (liquid or gas). Some components remain longer on the stationary phase than others, and separation is thereby achieved.

There are many different types of chromatographic procedures, such as the three used in CHE 327: **thin-layer chromatography (TLC)**, **gas (or gas-liquid) chromatography (GC)**, and **column chromatography**. However, there are only two types of separation mechanisms: adsorption and partition. Table 11.1 shows the classification of chromatographic methods based on experimental procedure and separation mechanism.

Table 11.1 Classification of chromatographic methods.

Chromatographic Method	Separation Mechanism	Mobile Phase	Stationary Phase
Gas-Liquid (GC)	Partition	Gas	Liquid
Gas-Solid (GC)	Adsorption	Gas	Solid
Column chromatography	Adsorption	Liquid	Solid adsorbent
Thin-layer chromatography	Adsorption	Liquid	Solid adsorbent
Liquid chromatography (LC)	Partition	Liquid	Liquid

Adsorption Chromatography

In **adsorption chromatography**, the substances being separated are first adsorbed onto the adsorbent (stationary phase), and then desorbed into the solvent (mobile phase) as the solvent passes through the adsorbent. The compounds and the solvent compete for the adsorbent. The success of the separation depends on the different polarities of three components: 1) adsorbent, 2) compounds, and 3) solvent.

Traditional adsorbents are silica (SiO_2) and alumina (Al_2O_3). Either of these adsorbents will always be the most polar phase. You will use silica in CHE 327.

Table 11.2 Compounds separated by chromatography.

Compounds	Functional Group(s)	Polarity
Alkanes and alkenes	RH, $R_2C=CR_2$	low
Aromatic hydrocarbons	Benzenoids	
Ethers	ROR	
Esters	RCOOR′	
Halogenated hydrocarbons	RX	
Aldehydes and ketones	RCH=O, $R_2C=O$	
Alcohols	ROH	
Amines	RNH_2, etc.	
Carboxylic acids	RCOOH	high

The compounds in the mixture will be of different polarities. You can make a tentative prediction of the polarity of a compound from its structure, considering the functional group(s). Table 11.2 lists the usual order of polarities of different types of compounds. **Usually polar compounds adhere to the polar adsorbent more strongly than less polar compounds, and therefore, are retained on the stationary phase longer**. It is easiest to separate compounds of widely different polarities.

Table 11.3 Common chromatography solvents.

Compounds	Formula	Polarity
Ligroin	C_nH_{2n+2}	low
Diethyl ether	$CH_3CH_2OCH_2CH_3$	
Ethyl acetate	$CH_3COOCH_2CH_3$	
Acetone	CH_3COCH_3	
Ethanol	CH_3CH_2OH	
Methanol	CH_3OH	
Acetic acid	CH_3COOH	high

The solvent or solvents will also be of different polarities, too. As listed in Table 11.3, you have a great deal of choice, not only of individual solvents, but of mixtures in various proportions.

You will use two adsorption chromatography techniques in CHE 327, thin-layer and column. More details will be discussed in the experimental instructions.

An Example of Separation

Consider a mixture of two compounds, one polar and one nonpolar. The mixture is applied to the adsorbent, which is the most polar phase. The polar compound is strongly adsorbed, the nonpolar compound less so.

In the following three cases, the solvent is changed from nonpolar to moderately polar to very polar. The result is that as the polarity of the solvent increases from case to case, the mobility of both compounds correspondingly increases; but the nonpolar compound always moves faster than the polar one (except in the third case where they move at the same rate).

Case 1: A nonpolar solvent is passed over the surface of the adsorbent. There is little effect on the polar compound, which adheres strongly. The nonpolar compound, however, is displaced by the solvent. The displacement occurs even if the nonpolar compound and the solvent are similar in polarity, simply because there is so much more of the solvent present. The polar compound moves little if at all, and the nonpolar compound moves to some extent.

Case 2: Now consider the same mixture and the same adsorbent treated with a more polar solvent. Both polar and nonpolar compounds are displaced more effectively than before. Both compounds move more than they did in the first case, the nonpolar one again is the faster of the two.

Case 3: With a solvent that is very polar, both compounds are swept from the adsorbent and move quickly at the same rate. This situation is not useful chromatographically, as no separation occurs.

Partition Chromatography

In **partition chromatography** (gas-liquid or liquid-liquid), the stationary phase is usually a liquid, which can be coated on the surface of an inert solid support. The substances being separated distribute themselves between the stationary liquid phase and the mobile liquid phase. The partition mechanism then can be explained exactly the same way as in extraction (see Chapter 9).

The GC (gas-liquid) chromatography you will use in CHE 327 is partition chromatography. More details will be discussed in section 11.4.

11.2 Thin-Layer Chromatography (TLC)

Like melting point, thin-layer chromatography, or TLC is an analytical technique, enabling you to get information about purity and identity from a very small sample.

In thin-layer chromatography, glass, plastic, or metal plates coated with a thin layer of adsorbent (silica in CHE 327) are used as the stationary phase. The mobile phase is a pure solvent or a mixture of several solvents.

General Procedure

To carry out a TLC analysis, a solution of the mixture to be separated is prepared, and a small amount is spotted at a position at the lower edge of the plate. Then the plate is placed in a closed chamber containing the **developing solvent** (this is the mobile phase), as shown in Figure 11.1. The solvent rises up the plate by capillary action – this process is called **development**. After the plate is removed from the chamber, the compounds will need to be **visualized** if they are colorless.

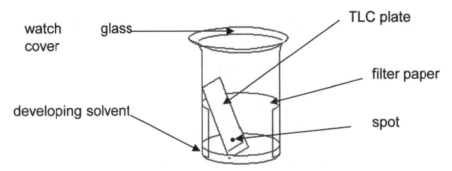

Figure 11.1 Developing chamber containing a TLC plate.

Here are the steps with some tips you should find helpful in CHE 327:

1. Preparing the solvent chamber.

    In CHE 327 your chamber is a cut-off 400 ml beaker closed with a watch glass. The air space is saturated with solvent vapor by using a piece of filter paper as a wick. Because the developing solvent is very important to the success of the TLC separation, do not contaminate it with acetone or water left over from cleaning the chamber.

2. Preparing the solution of the sample to be analyzed.

    An extremely small amount of sample is needed. Dissolve the sample in any volatile solvent that will do the job. This solvent does not have to be the same one as will be used in the development step. The solutions of the standards in CHE 327 experiments are prepared for you; you will have to prepare the solutions for your own materials.

3. Spotting the TLC plate.

    You will need a **micropipet** for each solution you will be transferring to the plate. Commercially available micropipets are similar to a thinner melting point tube but open at both ends.

    Handle your TLC plate by the edges only. If you get fingerprints on the silica (the powdery side), they may show up as confusing spots afterwards. Your fingerprints are organic materials.

    On the TLC plate, mark the **origin** 1 cm from the end. Do not scratch the silica surface. All marks on the TLC plate, here and later, should be in pencil – some inks will run in some solvents.

    Spotting is the method of transferring the solution to the plate. Dip the micropipet into the solution, which will be drawn up by capillary action. Supporting the heel of your hand on the bench top, hold the pipet almost perpendicular to the plate. Just touch the pipet to the silica and lift it as soon as you see solution running out to make a spot. It is desirable to keep the spot very small. You can practice spotting by using pure solvent since it will evaporate once applied to the silica.

If necessary, apply more solution at the same location after the first spotting has dried. You must use enough material so that you will be able to see the spots at the visualization stage. But keep in mind that having too much material will result in problems – spots will be too big and may overlap after development. Knowing the right amount is something that will come with experience; guidelines for the novice are given in the individual experiments.

4. Developing the TLC plate.

Slide the watch glass cover off slowly to avoid having turbulence develop in the vapor-saturated air space. Place the TLC plate almost vertically in the chamber, with the origin side down, as shown in Figure 11.1. The plate should touch glass only at its top and bottom. **The level of the solvent in the chamber should be below the spottings.** Otherwise, the compounds would wash into the bulk solvent, rather than be carried up the plate. For this reason, you were advised to fill the chamber to a depth of about 1/2 cm and to place the origin 1 cm from the end. Do not put more than one plate at a time in the chamber – this is asking for trouble.

Let the **solvent front** rise almost to the top of the plate – a 1/2 cm margin is recommended. Before the solvent goes over the top, remove the plate from the chamber; and as you do so, draw a line marking the front. Until you have mastered TLC, you may tend to forget this step, so remind yourself beforehand.

5. Evaporating the solvent.

Let the developing solvent evaporate from the plate before visualizing the spots, otherwise some solvents may also be visualized.

6. Visualizing the spots.

Some materials, such as the plant pigments, are already colored and will be visible against the white silica background with no further treatment needed.

However, many organic compounds are colorless and will need to be visualized. There are two common visualization methods (UV light will be used in CHE 327):

- **Ultraviolet (UV) light**. Some TLC plates have a fluorescent indicator, meaning that the plate itself will glow. Compounds that absorb UV light will appear dark against this bright background. Compounds that fluoresce at a different wavelength from the indicator will appear bright but a different color.

- **Iodine**. Many organic compounds form complexes with iodine vapor. These will show as brown spots after the TLC plate has been exposed to iodine for a few minutes.

All observations about visualization, including those with naturally visible materials, should be made after development as soon as possible. Compounds adsorbed on the silica, or their iodine complexes, may not be stable. Keep in mind that a compound may show up by both visualization methods, by only one, or by neither of them. Thus, a positive observation is usually reliable but a negative one is not necessarily so.

Safety Precautions

- Never use a Bunsen burner near flammable solvents.
- Evaporate the solvent from a developed TLC plate in a fume hood.
- Never look directly at an ultraviolet light source. Like the sun, it can cause damage to your eyes.
- Iodine is a strong irritant. Handle it with caution.

Interpreting TLC

Figure 11.2 is a drawing of a completed TLC plate. The mark 1 cm from the bottom indicates the origin, that is, the height at which two solutions were initially applied to positions A and B. The line 1/2 cm from the top indicates the solvent front, the height to which the solvent was allowed to rise.

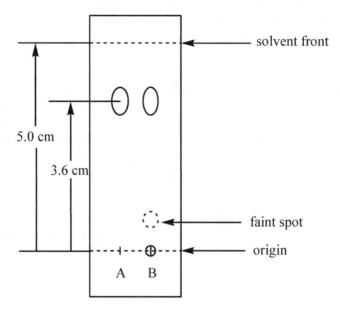

Figure 11.2 A developed TLC plate with visualized spots.

The spots are shown at their final positions, outlined exactly (not circled). There still remains some material at the origin in lane B, as is indicated by the spot there. The dotted outline in lane B marks a faint spot.

Interpretation: The material in lane A is pure, as shown by the TLC's single spot. The material in lane B has three components. One of the compounds in B is the same as the one in A, as shown by the match in the height the spots attain (see the definition of R_f below).

Caution!

The interpretation is not absolutely reliable. Two different compounds could happen to move at the same rate. Therefore, A could be a mixture that just happens to give a single spot. Or the spots that match in A and B could do so purely by accident.

The Retention Factor (R_f)

The **retention factor** (or $\mathbf{R_f}$) is a term that allows you to compare the mobility of different compounds. It is defined as the distance moved by the spot relative to that of the solvent front and expressed as a decimal fraction without units:

$$R_f = \frac{\text{distance traveled by the compound}}{\text{distance traveled by the solvent}}$$

To calculate the R_f value for a given compound, measure the distance that it moves from the origin to the center of the spot. As shown in Figure 11.2, this distance for the spot in lane A is 3.6 cm. The distance the solvent moves, also from the origin, is 5.0 cm; therefore, the R_f of the compound in sample A is 0.72 (no units). In other words, the compound moved 72 % of the distance traveled by the solvent from the origin.

Whenever you do TLC, run at least two trials on the same plate. The direct comparison this allows is useful because R_f values are not numerically reproducible from plate to plate.

11.3 Column Chromatography

Column chromatography is very similar to TLC in its principles and results but on a much larger scale. This technique is used to separate and isolate components rather than analyze their mixture.

General Procedure

The adsorbent is contained in a large glass (or sometimes metal) tube with a stopcock at the bottom, much like a buret without the markings. The advantage of having a stopcock is that the column can be interrupted, although not recommended for any length of time. A concern is that compounds, once separated, could re-mix by diffusion if left sitting too long. Also, if the column has cracks, the compounds could pool and re-mix in these spaces.

The mixture of compounds to be separated is applied to the top of the column. Then solvent is added and allowed to run through. In a classic column chromatography, the solvent is allowed to flow down unaided – this is called **gravity column chromatography**. Alternatively, the solvent is pushed down by air or nitrogen pressure; this technique is called **flash chromatography**.

With the similar separation mechanism to that of TLC, the components in the mixture move at different rates and are separated into different **bands**. The **eluate** (the liquid that runs through) is collected and analyzed by TLC.

These are the steps:

1. Analytical TLC before column chromatography.

    Before running a column, it is wise to check by TLC whether the separation can be expected to work. After all, if TLC shows that the components move too closely together, and trying less polar solvents does not solve the problem, there is little point wasting time and material by scaling up to a column. The analytical TLC should be run with the same adsorbent but perhaps a more polar solvent than you plan to use on the column.

2. Packing the column.

    The step where you add adsorbent to the column is called **packing**. The column is commonly packed by one of the following methods:

    - **Slurry packing**: The adsorbent is added to the solvent, and with stirring, the mixture is added to the column.
    - **Dry packing**: The solvent is added to the column before the dry adsorbent is slowly poured in, with tapping to mix.

    In both methods, care should be taken to mix the adsorbent gradually with the solvent. Otherwise, the heat of mixing is significant, the adsorbent settles unevenly in the convection currents of the liquid, and cracks form in the column.

3. Preparing the solution of the mixture.

    Generally you should use the same solvent to dissolve the mixture as you will be using to run the column. However, there may be the problem that the mixture will not dissolve in the solvent. In such a case, an alternative method must be used.

    For better separation, a minimum amount of the solvent should be used.

4. Loading the column.

    The step where you add the solution of your mixture to the column is called **loading**.

5. Running the column.

Once you begin running the column, try not to interrupt it. If you let the mixture of compounds sit on the column, even if they have begun separating, they can diffuse back together. For this reason, have your solvent ready and your collecting containers clean and labeled beforehand.

Pour the chromatography solvent into the column, and collect the eluate that comes through. Each portion that you collect in a separate container (test tubes in the *β-Carotene* experiment) is called a **fraction**. The first fractions usually are pure solvent.

In a successful column, the compounds that were initially together at the top of the column form a series of bands. These bands are visible when the compounds are colored. When the materials are colorless, you do not have such observations to guide you. Deciding where to cut the fractions is more difficult – partly accomplished by educated guessing, and aided by TLC taken periodically as the column progresses. In actual practice, this situation is much more common than the first.

You may simply allow gravity to pull the solvent through the column. However, there are two convenient methods to speed things up:

- Flash chromatography. Apply pressure to the top of the column. This makes the drip-rate faster.

- Change the solvent to a more polar one. The more polar the solvent, the faster all pigments move. Therefore, make the change gradually. For your small column, follow the experimental guidelines. Changing solvent gradually from less to more polar is often pre-planned in a separation of compounds of varying polarity.

6. Analyzing the results by TLC.

Microscale Column Chromatography in the β-Carotene Experiment

In the *β-Carotene* experiment, you run a micro-version of a column. Microscale chromatography is faster and more economical, and produces less waste than with a column of conventional size. For the column, a short Pasteur pipet containing silica is used – a pipet column is very convenient for small-scale separations. The solution of the pigment mixture is applied to the top of the silica.

Here are the steps with some comments you might find helpful (more details of this technique will be discussed in the context of the *β-Carotene* experiment):

1. Analyzing the mixture by TLC.

The goal of this experiment is to isolate β-carotene, so in the TLC you are looking for it to be well separated from the other pigments. Use ethyl acetate-ligroin for the TLC (but pure ligroin for the column).

2. Packing and setting up.

Pack the column by pouring dry silica into a short-stem Pasteur pipet. This simple method works well in the small-scale experiment.

3. Loading.

This is a case where you compromise by using ethyl acetate-ligroin instead of pure ligroin to dissolve the pigments. But because of the strong effect of the polar solvent, use it sparingly. Try to load the pigments straight onto the silica and wash them down with a minimum of ligroin. The idea is to start the run with the pigments in a narrow band at the top.

4. Running the column.

In this experiment, because the compounds are colored, the bands on column will be visible. Collect the β-carotene band in a separate test tube. It does not matter if you mingle in excess solvent either before or after, since this will be evaporated off later. However, it is important not to collect other pigments together in the same test tube as the carotene.

5. Analyzing the results by TLC.

Were you able to separate the β-carotene cleanly from the other pigments? You can answer this question by TLC, comparing the material in your fraction to a sample of the authentic compound.

> ### *Possible Problems in the β-Carotene Experiment – The Solvent Effect*
>
> In both TLC and column techniques, the way you control the separation is by choosing an appropriate solvent. However, if the solvent is too polar, the compounds will all move together at too fast a rate. Result: No separation.
>
> Although you are running the column in ligroin, the least polar of the available solvents, you could unwittingly contaminate it with one that is more polar. In the β-Carotene experiment, these are some possible sources of contamination:
>
> 1) Acetone, water, or ethanol from cleaning glassware
>
> 2) Water from spinach
>
> 3) Ethyl acetate from the extraction of the plant pigments, if not removed by rotary evaporation
>
> 4) Too much ethyl acetate-ligroin used to make the pigment solution and then loaded onto the column. The ligroin will not have any effect – it is the same as the column solvent – but the excess ethyl acetate could be a problem.

11.4 Gas Chromatography (GC)

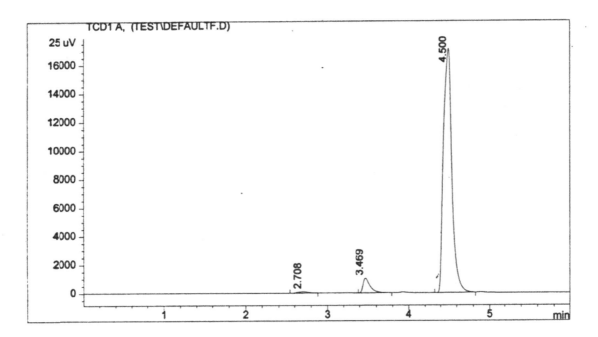

Figure 11.3 A typical gas chromatogram

The technique is gas chromatography, the instrument is the gas chromatograph, and the output is the **gas chromatogram** – all are called GC. Like TLC, GC is an analytical technique requiring very little material – our instruments may require as little as 0.1 μl (0.0001 ml) of liquid sample. As in all chromatography, there is the stationary phase (in the column) and the moving phase (the carrier gas). In our instruments, the column material is a high boiling nonpolar silicone oil and the carrier gas is helium.

To take a GC, you introduce the sample by syringe into the injector, where vaporization and mixing with the gas take place. The mixture passes to the column in the oven, where separation into different components takes place. The components then pass through the detector one after another, where each causes a peak to be recorded on the chromatogram.

The nonpolar column material dissolves the sample compounds, but those with low boiling points have higher vapor pressures over the solution. Thus, compounds tend to come off the column in the same order as they would distil. The relative size of each peak is a measure of its concentration in the sample.

GC is a good method for determining purity and analyzing mixtures; and since each peak appears at a characteristic position, it may confirm identity if a known sample is available for comparison.

Interpreting GC Chromatograms

A typical GC chromatogram is shown in Figure 11.3. A GC is read from left to right. The origin is the beginning of the run, that is, the point at which the injection was made. Each peak corresponds to a separate compound passing through the column.

Interpretation of the above chromatogram: The first small peak is most likely air and can be ignored. This sample has two significant components, whose x-axis positions are printed next to the peaks. A pure sample would have only one peak in addition to air.

As with TLC, interpret cautiously, since any single peak might correspond to two or more compounds that happen to come off at the same rate.

#	Compound Name	Amount	Resp.	Resp.%	Exp.RT	Meas.RT
1		0.000	778.993	0.589	0.000	2.708
2		0.000	5.981e3	4.526	0.000	3.469
3		0.000	1.254e5	94.884	0.000	4.500
Totals:		0.000				

Figure 11.4 Typical GC numerical information.

In addition to the chromatogram, you will receive a table with numerical information. Figure 11.4 is the one for the GC in Figure 11.3 on the previous page. The relevant columns are *resp. %* (response percent) and *meas. RT* (measured retention time, in units of minutes).

The instrumental response percent for each component is related to its percent in the mixture. For the thermal conductivity detectors of our instruments, the numerical values are accurate to within 10%. If greater accuracy is needed, it can be achieved by 1) factoring out the air peak, and 2) calibrating with standards of known concentration.

The **retention time** is how long a compound spends on the column; on a nonpolar column, higher boiling compounds have greater retention times. This property is analogous to R_f in comparing mobility of different components of a mixture. Like R_f values, retention times are not strictly reproducible, although if none of the conditions are changed, the values tend to be reasonably consistent.

Factors Affecting GC Separation

There are two major factors affecting GC separation:

- The nature of the column material. In CHE 327, we use a nonpolar column that separates on the basis of boiling point. There are other types of columns that separate on the basis of polarity; these might be more useful depending on the problem at hand.

- The temperature of the column. If the setting is too high, different compounds can give peaks too close together or even only one peak. If the setting is too low, the compounds will separate well but give broad peaks, and the GC run time is inconveniently long. Often, a suitable temperature is approximately 20 °C below the boiling point of the major component. In CHE 327, all of the instrument temperatures are pre-set according to the boiling points of the different esters.

Use of the GC Instrument

Here is the summary of GC instrument instructions:

1. Check and record the instrument settings. Relevant data are the column material and the temperature of the injector, oven, and detector.

2. Check the sample – water droplets, cloudiness, or particles must be removed before you use the syringe.

3. The stockroom manager or a TA will inject your sample. We use the "wet needle" method, where we draw the liquid sample into the syringe and squirt it back out. The amount of residual sample that remains on the syringe needle is enough for the GC instrument to detect. The needle is injected into the instrument and removed in one swift motion. The "start" button is then immediately pushed on the GC keypad.

4. Let the GC run either until there is as much baseline after the last peak as before it or for about three minutes total. These are reasonable periods, but there is never a guarantee that all peaks have emerged during the time you have allowed.

5. The syringe is cleaned between each injection with acetone.

GC in the Ester Experiment

In the *Ester* experiment, GC will be useful in determining whether your ester is pure. However, keep in mind the limitations of the technique:

- If a contaminant is non-volatile, for example grease, it will not show up in the GC even though it may be visually apparent.

- If a contaminant is a separate phase so that it does not enter the syringe when you draw up the liquid, it will not show in the GC.

- If a contaminant has the same retention time as the ester, its peak will coincide with that of the ester and its presence will not be detected.

The first peak coming off, if it is small, is due to air. However, if it is large, it corresponds to a low-boiling contaminant such as ether or acetone, having the same retention time as the air and overlapping with it.

Besides being used to determine purity, GC can also be used to help identify a compound. If you had an authentic sample of the same ester as the one you synthesized, you could prepare a mixture of a drop of each. Obtaining a single peak for such a mixture is good evidence (although not proof) that the two compounds are the same. This procedure, called **co-injection**, is analogous to running two samples side-by-side on a TLC plate and seeing if the R_f values match. Since usually the identity of the ester is not in question in CHE 327, and our instruments are of limited availability, you will not be performing a co-injection.

Chapter 12   INFRARED (IR) SPECTROSCOPY

12.1 The Electromagnetic Spectrum

Molecules absorb electromagnetic radiation over a broad range of wavelengths. Some regions where this property is particularly useful in analytical work are shown in Table 12.1.

Table 12.1 Selected regions of the electromagnetic spectrum.

Wavelength*	Spectral Region
~200-400 nm	Ultraviolet
~400-800 nm	Visible
~2.5-15 μ	Infrared
~1-5 m	Radio (NMR)

*One micron (μ) = 10^{-6} m = 10^3 nanometers (nm).

Modern infrared spectroscopy uses wavenumber $\overline{\nu}$ units instead of wavelength λ.

$$\overline{\nu} = 1/\lambda$$

The unit of wavenumber is the inverse centimeter (cm^{-1}). The 2.5-15 μ IR range corresponds to 4000-650 cm^{-1}.

12.2 Infrared (IR) Spectroscopy

The technique is infrared spectroscopy, the instrument is the spectrometer, and the output is the **spectrum** (plural **spectra**) – all are called IR.

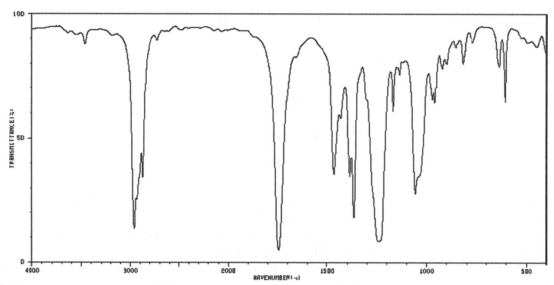

Figure 12.1 The IR spectrum of an ester

A molecule can absorb radiation of only certain allowed energies.   If radiation over a range of energies (for example, 4000-650 cm^{-1} in the IR) is passed through a sample, the record of which energies are absorbed and which transmitted is the spectrum. The x-axis of an IR spectrum consists of peaks (also called bands) in regions of absorption and baseline in regions of transmission. The y-axis shows percent transmittance.

As energy is absorbed at certain wavenumbers, it goes into the vibration of individual bonds. A peak at high wavenumber (high energy) means the bond is strong. A high-intensity peak means something different, that the bond's dipole moment is greatly affected.

The spectrum of an ester shown in Figure 12.1 illustrates the features described above.

The IR spectrum can be broken down into two regions. Between roughly 4000-1450 cm^{-1} is the **functional group region** of the IR spectrum, where peaks corresponding to vibrational energy of individual bonds can be identified. From 1450 cm^{-1} down, the energy absorbed goes into increasing the vibrational energy of the molecule as a whole. This is the **fingerprint region**, where each kind of molecule has a distinctive pattern.

Thus, you can interpret an IR spectrum to find out what kind of molecule you have, not only its functional groups but something about its carbon-carbon bonds. You can match an IR spectrum to one in the literature to identify specifically which molecule you have among structurally similar candidates. A band-for-band match in the fingerprint region of your IR spectrum to a literature IR spectrum is considered very strong evidence of a compound's identity (because of end absorption, you can ignore the region below 500 cm^{-1}).

12.3 Interpreting IR Spectra

One of the most common uses of IR is confirming the identity of a compound. IR frequencies are characterized according to stretching (and other vibrational modes) of different types of bonds. An absorption frequency table like Table 12.2 will help you identify what functional group(s) is(are) present in the compound being analyzed.

The absorptions are listed in decreasing wavenumber order. However, rather than work down the list, you should interpret your IR systematically according to the following three-step plan:

1. Is there a carbonyl group in the 1750-1650 region?

   If so, what kind of carbonyl is it? Look for the aldehyde H-C(=O) stretching at ~2700 cm^{-1} or the broad carboxylic acid O-H stretching between 3400-2500 cm^{-1}. If these are absent, the compound may be a ketone or ester. The ester C-O stretching between 1300-1000 cm^{-1} is sometimes helpful but not always because of so many other groups present in the fingerprint region.

   A carbonyl bond interacts with other parts of the molecule, and this interaction may change the peak position:

   - If the bond is part of an ester, the carbonyl peak is higher than normal, about 1735 cm^{-1}. Other functional groups not met in CHE 327, such as anhydrides or amides, also have non-normal peak positions.

   - If the bond is conjugated with an alkenyl or aromatic double bond, the carbonyl C=O stretching may be lower than normal.

   - If the bond is in a small ring, the carbonyl C=O stretching may be higher than normal.

     Example: cyclopentanone C=O   about 1740 cm^{-1}

     Example: cyclobutanone C=O about 1780 cm^{-1}

   If there is no carbonyl, move to the next step.

2. Is there a hydroxyl or amine group in the 3600-3200 cm^{-1} region?

   If so, a double peak means NH$_2$ (H-N-H) stretching, and a single peak can be either O-H or N-H stretching. Beware: A tertiary amine NR$_3$ has no N-H bonds and no N-H absorption in its IR spectrum!

A confirming peak for alcohols is the C-O stretch between 1300-1000 cm^{-1}. A confirming peak for primary amines is the H-N-H bending about 1600 cm^{-1}.

Once the carbonyl and OH/NH questions have been answered, move to the next step.

3. What kind of carbon-carbon bonds are present?

Look for alkenyl/aromatic C-H stretching between 3000-3050 cm^{-1}. If these are present, there should also be C=C stretching between 1650-1450 cm^{-1}, either alkenyl or aromatic. Keep in mind that most organic compounds have alkyl groups which you should expect to see between 3000-2800 cm^{-1}.

You should practice applying these interpretive methods to the sample spectra shown in section 12.6.

Table 12.2 Characteristic IR absorptions of functional groups (all peak positions are approximate).

Type of Vibration	Peak Position (cm^{-1})	Features	IR Region
Alcohol O-H stretching	3600-3200	Strong and broad.	
N-H stretching	3500-3100	NH$_2$ (two bands), NH (one band)	
Acid O-H stretching	3400-2500	Strong and broad. Can overlap with other peaks.	
Alkenyl C-H stretching	3100-3010		
Aromatic C-H stretching	3080-3020		
Alkyl C-H stretching	3000-2800		
Aldehyde C-H (H-C=O) stretching	2770-2700	Sharp but often weak.	functional group region
Carbonyl C=O stretching	1750-1710	Strong and sharp. Position dependent on type of C=O function and degree of unsaturation. Lowered by conjugation.	
Alkenyl C=C stretching	1650	Lowered by conjugation. May be weak.	
Amine N-H bending	1600-1540	May be weak. Weaker for secondary amine.	
Aromatic C=C stretching	1600-1450	Usually two to three sharp peaks.	
C-O stretching	1300-1000	Strong.	

The IR technique is used in the *Ester* experiment to help identify your ester product.

12.4 Preparing Liquid Samples for IR

In CHE 327, only liquid samples are analyzed by IR spectroscopy. You will need the following accessories to take the IR spectrum of a neat (pure) liquid:

- A pair of sodium chloride plates
- A Pasteur pipet for applying the liquid sample
- Ligroin, with its own pipet
- Kimwipes (tissues)

All of the accessories will be provided for you in the instrument room, except for the Pasteur pipet used for applying the liquid sample. **You must make sure you bring a clean and dry pipet**. The sodium chloride plates which support your sample are transparent to IR light. They are expensive and fragile. Examine them for defects before using them. You are responsible for maintaining the plates in the same condition as received. Obviously, salt plates are water-soluble. They are sensitive even to the little bit of moisture on your fingertips or in the air. Handle them by the edges and as infrequently as possible, and keep them in their case when they are not being used.

You may decide it is necessary to pre-clean the plates. Place them on a tissue and wash them with several baths of ligroin. Acetone is not used for cleaning since acetone contains water. Dab the plates with a tissue in between washes to soak up the ligroin – avoid skin contact. Work quickly so that water doesn't condense on the plates, rub them dry, and immediately apply the sample as described in the next step.

Put one salt plate on a Kimwipe tissue. Obtain a sample with a Pasteur pipet dipped into the liquid, and apply it to the center of the plate (only one small drop is required); carefully cover with the other plate and rotate so that there is a thin sandwich of liquid between them. Finally place the assembly in the IR beam and record the spectrum.

At the end, slide the plates apart and put them dirty side up on a tissue. Clean as before, allow to air dry for about a minute, and put them in their case.

Problems from Water

Problems from water are of several types, and they have been mentioned in the paragraph above and also in the *Ester* experiment. Be alert to diagnose, and if necessary, correct for them.

- Water will damage the salt plates. However, because most organic liquids are immiscible with water, you can usually detect its presence in a sample by cloudiness or droplets. You should remove all visible water before taking IR.

- Water will affect your IR interpretation because it contains the OH group which absorbs in its characteristic region of the spectrum. A completely clear (that is, transparent) sample of a water-immiscible compound is likely to be water-free. This situation is true for your ester product. However, there might still be a problem from atmospheric water condensed on the plates, especially on a humid day, aggravated by the cooling that occurs as the wash acetone evaporates. If you suspect that the problem is with the plates and not the sample, rub the plates dry and take a new IR spectrum as speedily as possible.

12.5 The IR Instrument

Our teaching laboratories utilize modern Fourier transform infrared spectrometers. The following brief description of FTIR is taken from Kemp, W. *Organic Spectroscopy*, third edition. New York: W. H. Freeman, 1991, 45.

In FTIR, the infrared light is passed through a scanning Michelson interferometer, and Fourier transformation gives a plot of intensity versus frequency. A sample compound placed in the beam absorbs certain frequencies so that their intensities are reduced in the interferogram. The resulting Fourier transform is the IR absorption spectrum of the sample. Because of the immense literature that exists in which transmittance $[A = \log (1/T)]$ is plotted versus wavenumber, we continue to present the FTIR spectra in this mode.

12.6 Sample IR Spectra of Organic Compounds

Figures 12.2-11 show IR spectra reproduced from the Japanese National Institute of Advanced Industrial Science and Technology http://riodb01.ibase.aist.go.jp/sdbs/cgi-bin/cre_index.cgi?lang=eng.

Spectra are presented in the following order, to show the following features:

- The carbon skeleton: alkane, alkene, aromatic C-H and C=C

- The region to the left of CH: OH, NH_2

- The carbonyl group: ketone, aldehyde, carboxylic acid

- IR used to diagnose a problem: an aldehyde contaminated by a carboxylic acid

Remember to use the three-step interpretive method in section 12.3 when analyzing your spectrum.

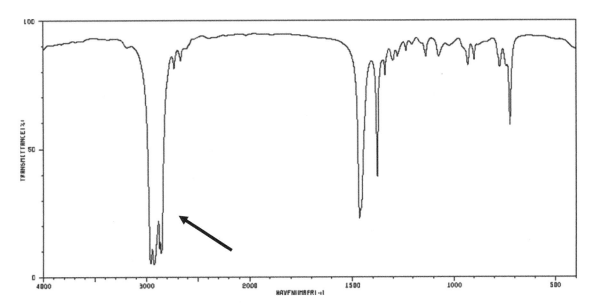

Figure 12.2 IR spectrum of heptane $CH_3(CH_2)_5CH_3$.

Simplicity is informative – in Figure 12.2 it means the lack of functional groups. The C-H stretching bands are visible between 2950-2850 cm^{-1} (see the arrow).

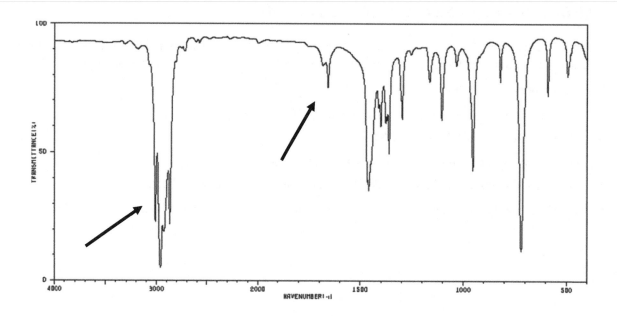

Figure 12.3 IR spectrum of *cis*-4-methyl-2-pentene CH$_3$CH=CHCH(CH$_3$)$_2$.

In Figure 12.3, as the arrows show, the alkenyl =C-H stretching of *cis*-4-methyl-2-pentene is visible at 3010 cm^{-1} and the C=C stretching at 1660 cm^{-1}. As is often the case, the C=C stretching is weak.

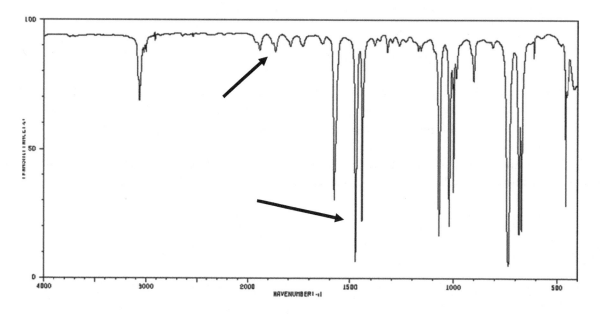

Figure 12.4 IR spectrum of bromobenzene C$_6$H$_5$Br.

In Figure 12.4, the aromatic =C-H stretching of bromobenzene is visible at ~3050-3080 cm^{-1}. The aromatic C=C stretching bands are seen at about 1445, 1475, and 1575 cm^{-1}. Additional diagnostic aromatic peaks are the overtones in the region 2000-1700 cm^{-1}.

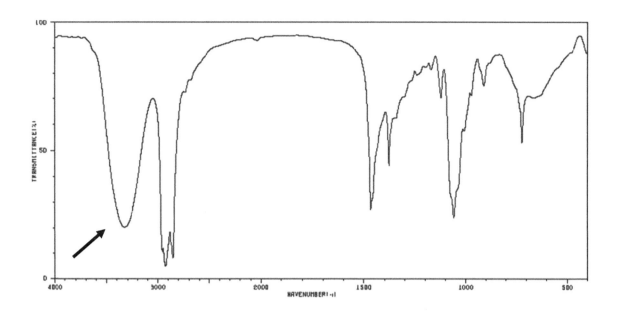

Figure 12.5 IR spectrum of 1-nonanol $CH_3(CH_2)_8OH$.

Here in Figure 12.5, the O-H stretching of 1-nonanol spans the region 3500-3050 cm^{-1}. Note that the peak at 1460 cm^{-1} doesn't denote aromatic C=C stretching since the corresponding aromatic C-H stretching bands between 3000-3050 cm^{-1} are absent.

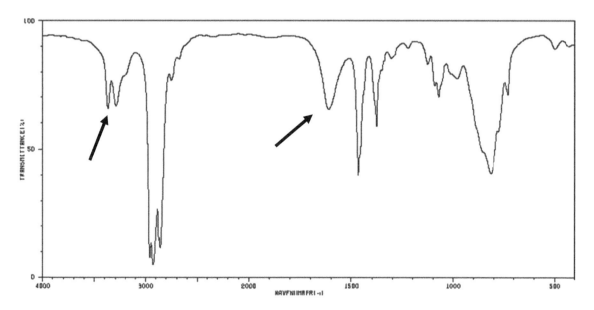

Figure 12.6 IR spectrum of 1-pentylamine $CH_3(CH_2)_4NH_2$.

In Figure 12.6, the two peaks at 3295 and 3370 cm^{-1} are the N-H stretching typical of a primary amine. The peak at 1615 cm^{-1} is the N-H bend.

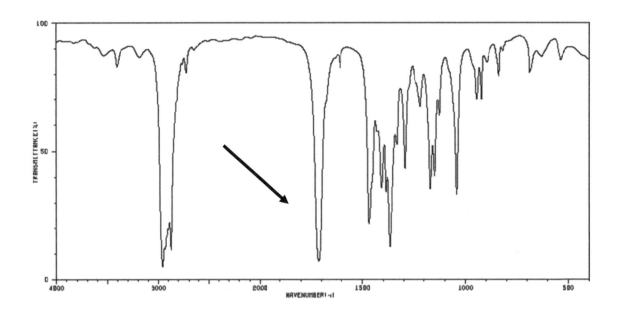

Figure 12.7 IR spectrum of 2,6-dimethyl-4-heptanone [(CH₃)₂CHCH₂]₂C=O.

In the IR spectrum of 2,6-dimethyl-4-heptanone as shown in Figure 12.7, the strong carbonyl C=O stretching is seen at the typical position of about 1715 cm⁻¹.

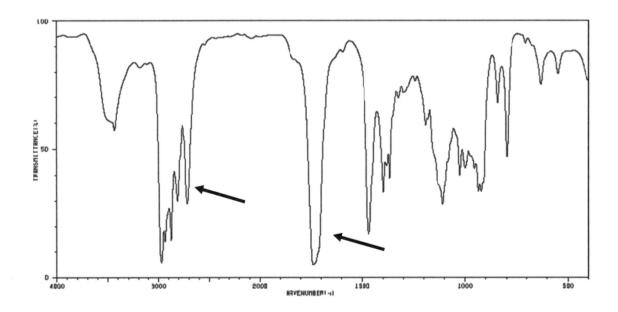

Figure 12.8 IR spectrum of 2-methylpropanal (CH₃)₂CHCH=O.

In the IR spectrum of 2-methylpropanal as shown in Figure 12.8, the diagnostic aldehyde C-H stretching is seen at about 2715 cm⁻¹ just to the right of the normal alkyl C-H peaks. The strong carbonyl C=O stretching is seen at ~1730 cm⁻¹. Also note the strong overtones (or maybe some water) in the O-H region.

78

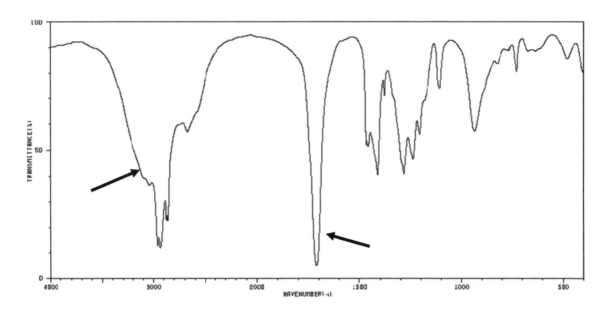

Figure 12.9 IR spectrum of heptanoic acid CH₃(CH₂)₅COOH.

In the IR spectrum of heptanoic acid shown in Figure 12.9, the strong carbonyl C=O stretching is seen at ~1710 cm⁻¹. From about 3500-2500 cm⁻¹, the O-H of the carboxylic acid group overlaps the C-H region.

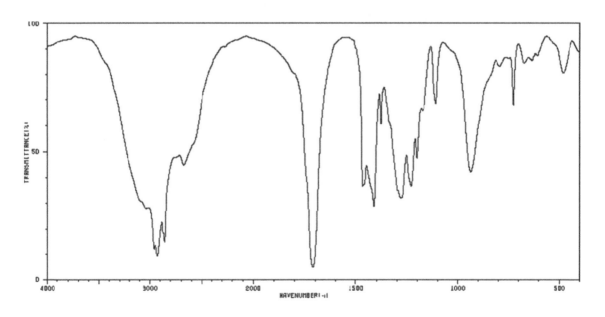

Figure 12.10   IR spectrum of octanoic acid CH₃(CH₂)₆COOH.

The IR spectrum of octanoic is shown in Figure 12.10; the strong carbonyl C=O stretching is at ~1710 cm⁻¹. The O-H of the carboxylic acid between 3500-2500 cm⁻¹ overlaps the C-H region.

Compare the two spectra on Figures 12.9 and 12.10. Here is a dramatic example of the fact that compounds with similar structures have similar spectra. Although an IR match is powerful evidence of identity, it must be confirmed with other information!

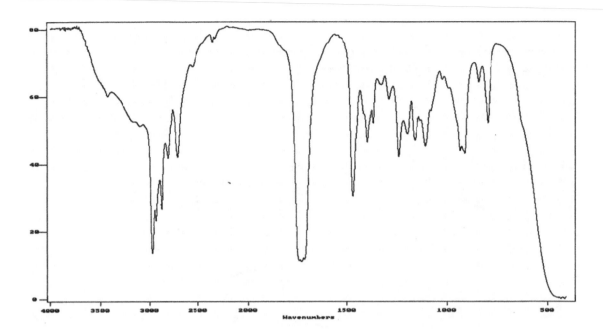

Figure 12.11 IR spectrum of 2-methylpropanal contaminated with 2-methylpropanoic acid (compare to the IR of pure 2-methylpropanal in Figure 12.8) $(CH_3)_2CHCH=O + (CH_3)_2CHCOOH$.

Aldehydes can easily air-oxidize to carboxylic acids. The IR spectrum above in Figure 12.11 gives evidence that this has occurred in the sample. The diagnostic aldehyde C-H is seen at 2710 cm^{-1}. The carboxylic acid O-H overlaps the entire C-H region. The aldehyde and acid C=O appear as one merged peak in the carbonyl region. The fingerprint region as well contains bands from both compounds.

Chapter 13   NUCLEAR MEGNATIC RESONANCE (NMR) SPECTROSCOPY

13.1 Introduction

In Chapter 12, we discussed the electromagnetic spectrum, and the energy absorption (or transmission) by the molecules when the radiation from the infrared region is applied to them. In this chapter, we will focus on nuclear magnetic resonance (NMR), the absorption of radio-frequency radiation by molecules in a strong magnetic field.

13.2 Nuclear Magnetic Resonance (NMR) Spectroscopy

Nuclear magnetic resonance (NMR) and infrared (IR) are two widely used spectroscopic tools in organic chemistry as both provide information about molecular structure. Compared to IR spectroscopy, NMR spectroscopy is more useful in revealing molecular structure as it gives information about the connectivity of the atoms. Therefore, NMR is routinely used in organic chemistry to determine the structure of more complicated organic compounds.

When placed in a magnetic field, a compound containing NMR active nuclei (such as ^1H, ^{13}C, ^{19}F) absorb electromagnetic radiation through the process known as magnetic resonance. Such absorption of energy is recorded to produce a characteristic spectrum of the compound. By interpreting the NMR spectrum of a compound, the structure of this compound can be determined.

In a typical NMR spectrum, there are three important parts:

- **chemical shift** – the location of the signals (on the x-axis)
- **integration** – the area under each signal in a NMR spectrum
- **coupling** – the signal splitting caused by interactions between nonequivalent nuclei

Chemical Shift

Chemical shift is the position of a signal on the x-axis. It depends on the strength of the external magnetic field and the frequency of the radiation applied, which is different from IR spectroscopy. A reference (or standard) compound is added to the sample so that the locations of the sample signals can be decided relative to the signal(s) from the reference (or standard). Tetramethylsilane (TMS) and some common organic solvents are often used as the references.

Chemical shift is measured using a delta (δ) scale, with a unit of parts per million (ppm). When a signal occurs on the left in a NMR spectrum (that is, it has a larger chemical shift), it is called a **downfield** signal; a signal occurs on the right is called an **upfield** signal. All the nuclei in the same structural environment have same chemical shift in a NMR spectrum and they are called structurally equivalent nuclei.

Table 13.1 lists the ^1H NMR signals for protons in most common organic compounds.

Integration

Integration is the area under each signal in a NMR spectrum and it is proportional to the number of nuclei producing the signal. Since all the structurally equivalent nuclei have the same chemical shift, the total integration of that signal corresponds to the number of the nuclei.

Coupling (Signal Splitting)

Coupling, or signal splitting, is another important feature of a NMR spectrum. Coupling is caused by the nonequivalent nuclei that are close to (usually within two or three bonds of) the nuclei producing the NMR signal. A signal having only one peak is called a **singlet**. A signal with two equal intensity peaks is called a **doublet**. A signal consisting of three signals with an intensity ratio of 1:2:1 is called a **triplet**, while a signal having four signals with intensities of 1:3:3:1 is called a **quartet**. In general, when an individual signal is split due to coupling with "n" adjacent nuclei, the number of lines in its splitting pattern is n + 1, and this is often called "n+1 rule".

Table 13.1 Approximate chemical shifts protons.*

Type of Proton	Chemical Shift (δ, ppm)
1° Alkyl RCH_3	0.8-1.0
2° Alkyl RCH_2R	1.2-1.4
3° Alkyl R_3CH	1.4-1.7
Allylic, $R_2C=C-CH_3$ | R	1.6-1.9
Ketone, $RCCH_3$ ‖ O	2.1-2.6
Benzylic, $ArCH_3$	2.2-2.5
Acetylenic, $RC{\equiv}CH$	2.5-3.1
Alkyl iodide, RCH_2I	3.1-3.3
Ether, $ROCH_2R$	3.3-3.9
Alcohol, $HOCH_2R$	3.3-4.0
Alkyl bromide, RCH_2Br	3.4-3.6
Alkyl chloride, RCH_2Cl	3.6-3.8
Vinylic, $R_2C=CH_2$	4.6-5.0
Vinylic, $R_2C=CH$ | R	5.2-5.7
Aromatic, ArH	6.0-8.5
Aldehyde, RCH ‖ O	9.5-10.5
Alcohol hydroxyl, ROH	0.5-6.0**
Amino, $R-NH_2$	1.0-5.0**
Phenolic, $ArOH$	4.5-7.7**
Carboxylic, $RCOH$ ‖ O	10-13**

* Solomons and Fryhle, *Organic Chemistry*, tenth edition, Wiley, 2009

**The chemical shifts of these protons vary in different solvents and with temperature and concentration.

The ^{1}H NMR spectrum of 2-butanone (Figure 13.1) below is a good example illustrating these different splitting pattern. The signal at δ ~ 1.1 ppm corresponds to the three protons (labeled as A) on the methyl group next to the methylene group, the signal at δ ~ 2.1 ppm corresponds to the three protons (labeled as B) on the methyl group adjacent to the carbonyl group; the signal at δ ~ 2.4 ppm corresponds to the two protons (labeled as C) on the methylene group adjacent to the methyl group. The signals appear as triplet, singlet, and quartet, from upfield to downfield, as there are split by two (n = 2), zero (n = 0), and three (n = 3) protons on adjacent carbon atoms, respectively.

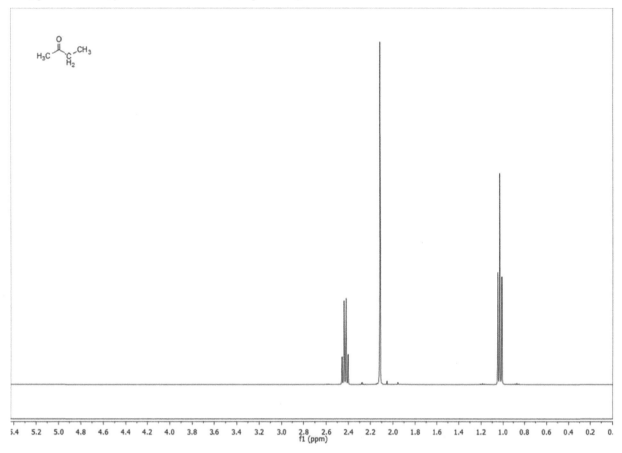

Figure 13.1 The ^{1}H NMR spectrum of 2-butanone in CDCl$_3$.

13.3 Interpreting ^{1}H-NMR Spectra

The common uses of NMR include elucidating the structure of unknown compounds and confirming the identity of compounds, known or unknown. To interpret a 1H NMR, you should follow the five-step process from Solomons and Fryhle, *Organic Chemistry*, tenth edition, Wiley, 2009:

1. Count the number of signals to determine how many unique protons there are in the molecule.
2. Use the chemical shift table (Table 13.1) to correlate chemical shifts with possible structural environments.
3. Determine the relative peak area of each signal as an indication of the relative number of protons producing the signal.
4. Interpret the splitting pattern of each signal to determine how many protons are present on carbons adjacent to those producing the signal, and sketch possible molecular fragments.
5. Join the fragments to make a molecule consistent with the data.

13.4 Sample ^{1}H NMR Spectra of Organic Compounds

Figures 13.2-3 show ^{1}H NMR spectra of some organic compounds or solvents used in our organic chemistry laboratories. Remember to use the five-step interpretive method in section 13.3 when analyzing your spectrum.

Figure 13.2 is the ^{1}H NMR spectrum of ethyl acetate, a common organic solvent. There are three different groups of protons: the protons on the methyl (CH_3) group next to the carbonyl group, the protons on the methyl (CH_3) group adjacent to the methylene (CH_2) group, and the protons on the methylene (CH_2) group. According to Table 13.1, the signal at $\delta \sim 1.3$ ppm corresponds to the protons on the CH_3 group adjacent to the CH_2 group, the signal at $\delta \sim 2.1$ ppm corresponds to the protons on the CH_3 group next to the carbonyl group, the signal at $\delta \sim 4.1$ ppm corresponds to the protons on the CH_2 group, which agrees with the relative peak area shown in the integration (3:3:2). The splitting pattern also confirms such assignment of the signals: the signal at $\delta \sim 1.3$ ppm is split to a triplet by the two protons on the adjacent CH_2 group, the signal at $\delta \sim 2.1$ ppm is a singlet as there is no proton on the adjacent carbonyl group, the signal at $\delta \sim 4.1$ ppm is split to a quarter by the three protons on the adjacent CH_3 group, all following the "n + 1 rule".

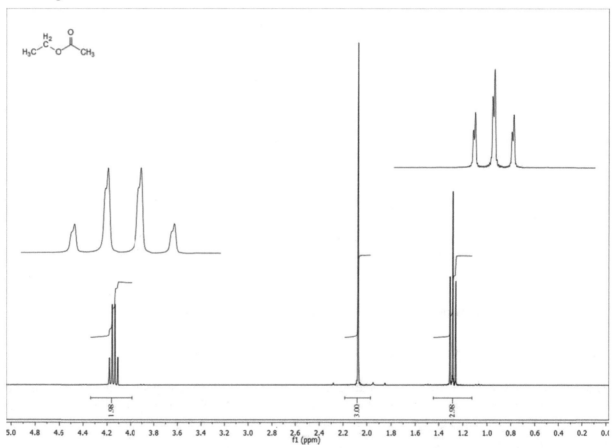

Figure 13.2 The ^{1}H NMR spectrum of ethyl acetate in $CDCl_3$.

The ^{1}H NMR spectrum of benzaldehyde, a compound used in CHE 384, is shown in Figure 13.3. There are generally two different kinds of protons: the aromatic protons on benzene ring, and the aldehyde proton. According to Table 13.1, the signals in the region between $\delta \sim 7.5$ ppm and $\delta \sim 7.8$ ppm correspond to the five protons on the benzene ring, the signal at $\delta \sim 10.0$ ppm corresponds to the aldehyde proton, which agrees with the relative peak area shown in the integration (approximately 5:1). The signal at $\delta \sim 10.0$ ppm is a singlet as there is no proton on the adjacent carbonyl group, while the splitting pattern of aromatic protons usually is not discussed in details in CHE 327. Nevertheless, the NMR

84

spectrum provides adequate information (the chemical shift and integration) to confirm the structure of benzaldehyde.

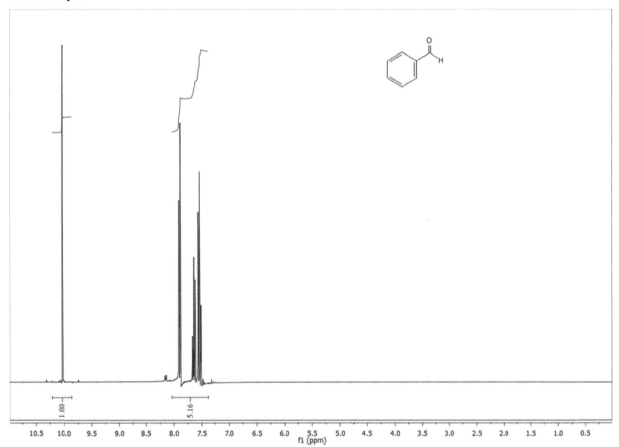

Figure 13.3 The ^{1}H NMR spectrum of benzaldehyde in CDCl$_3$.

Part 3 Experiments

Experiment 1   SIMPLE DISTILLATION

In this experiment, you will perform a distillation of a mixture of two liquids and measure the temperature change, without actually separating the two liquids. The purpose of this technique experiment is: 1) to observe the distillation behavior of a homogeneous liquid mixture, and 2) to develop the basic distillation skill often used in organic synthesis.

Background Reading

Read Chapter 6 about the distillation technique. Also review "heating mantle" in section 3.3.

Webpage Demonstration

A PowerPoint demonstration about the distillation setup is available on Blackboard. You may wish to print this out (six frames to a page is convenient) for reference during the lab period.

Properties of New Materials

Name	Appearance	Boiling Point (°C)	Hazard Statements
95% Ethanol	Colorless liquid	78	Flammable
			Skin and eye irritation
Water	Colorless liquid	100	-------------

Safety Precautions

- If you break a thermometer, inform the lab staff so they can deal with the broken glass, and mercury hazard (if any). Do not attempt cleanup yourself.
- Never plug the heating mantle into the wall socket.
- Never distill to dryness.

Pre-Lab Study Questions

Always ask yourself what is the purpose of each step in the procedure. In addition, consider the following for this experiment.

1. What is a liquid's boiling point? What is normal boiling point?

2. How is a compound's boiling point affected by its molecular structure?

3. Why should a distilling flask be at least about one-third full but no more than half full?

4. What would be the effect on temperature measurement of a thermometer that was positioned too high? Too low? Explain.

5. Why is it dangerous to heat a closed system containing volatiles?

Experimental Procedures

Part A Apparatus Assembly for Simple Distillation

<u>Step in procedure</u> | <u>Comments</u>

1) Set up a distillation as shown in Figure E1.1 and also on the webpage.

If you break a thermometer, inform your TAs so they can deal with the broken glass and mercury hazard. Do not attempt cleanup yourself.

a) In a 100 ml round bottom flask (rbf), put 15 mL 95% ethanol, 15 mL tap water, and a boiling stone.

Generally a distilling flask should be at least about one-third full but no more than half full.

Having a boiling stone will prevent the liquid from violent distillation (also called bumping).

b) Clamp the rbf (the "pot") containing the ethanol-water mixture to a ring stand at a height of about 10 cm from the base.

<u>It is necessary to clamp at the neck of any flask that is heated</u>. Support of the flask allows quick removal of the heat source should the reaction begin to go out of control.

c) Support a 100 mL heating mantle on a ring and fit the mantle as snugly as possible to the flask.

Any space between the sides of the rbf and the heating mantle can be filled with an aluminum foil collar. **Never place foil underneath the rbf** – you could start a fire.

d) Plug the heating mantle into a Variac; the switch should be in the off position.

With the Variac, you will be able to control the voltage, and thus the range of heating and the maximum temperature attainable. **Never plug the heating mantle into the wall socket** – you could start a fire.

e) <u>Lightly</u> grease the ground glass joint that will be connected.

Greasing will allow for later ease of disassembly. Be moderate. Remember that too much grease will dissolve in the product and contaminate it.

f) Insert the thermometer into its cap, and then slip on the o-ring <u>below</u> the cap.

Be sure to place the o-ring in the proper position so that a seal is created.

g) Connect the thermometer and cap to the distillation apparatus; connect the assembly to the rbf; adjust the thermometer position.

In distillation, you will be sure to get an accurate boiling point only if <u>the top of the thermometer bulb is level with the bottom of the side arm</u>, as shown by the dotted line in Figure E1.1.

To ensure that the thermometer does not touch the inside glass wall of the apparatus, you may need to support the upper stem against a clamp on the ring stand.

h) Place a 50 mL graduated cylinder below the drip tip of the distillation apparatus.

If the first graduation on your cylinder is above 2 mL, you will need to fill the cylinder with water up to a convenient graduation. **Make sure to record the start volume** so that you can keep track of the actual volume of distillate that will be collected.

i) Connect hoses to the condenser, and connect the bottom one to the faucet.

Use the clear thin-walled hosing instead of the red thick-walled hosing. The first is more flexible and less likely to be forced off by high water pressure.

j) Turn on the water faucet and adjust the flow to a gentle stream.

Too high a water pressure can force the hoses off in the next step, causing a flood.

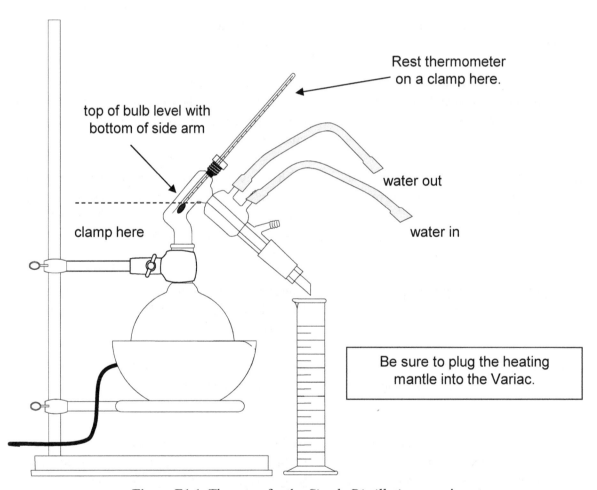

Rest thermometer on a clamp here.

top of bulb level with bottom of side arm

water out

clamp here

water in

Be sure to plug the heating mantle into the Variac.

Figure E1.1 The setup for the *Simple Distillation* experiment.

Part B Simple Distillation of an Ethanol-Water Mixture

Step in procedure	Comments
1) To begin distillation, turn on the Variac and adjust the setting.	The Variac setting depends on the boiling temperature of the liquid. You should try a low setting (about 50-60 V or 15-20%, depending on the type of Variac being used) initially since ethanol has a relatively low boiling point.
2) Observe the rise of the vapor head (the liquid-vapor line) and adjust the thermometer if necessary.	As the liquid begins to boil, the vapor head will rise until it reaches the bottom of the side arm (the position shown by the dotted line in Figure E1.1). If you have placed your thermometer correctly, the bulb will be <u>completely</u> bathed by liquid and vapor in equilibrium.
3) Adjust the rate of distillation to reach a moderate, steady distillation rate.	A relatively slower dripping rate (1 drop about every 4 or 5 seconds) is recommended here so that you can accurately measure T_{head} and receive better results.
	To adjust the rate, you may need to raise or lower the Variac setting. If necessary, you may insulate the rbf and distillation head against lab drafts. A tent of aluminum foil is good for this purpose, but be sure the foil does not touch the glass. Leave open a small flap so that you can view the liquid remaining in the pot. Save the foil at the end.
4) Collect the distillate in the 50 mL graduated cylinder.	In a table in your notebook, at intervals of <u>2 mL</u>, record the volume of the distillate and the corresponding boiling temperature measured on the thermometer head (T_{head}). **If you added water to your cylinder before distillation, make the necessary adjustments.**
5) Stop distilling when you have collected at least 26 mL of distillate or if there is a small amount of liquid remaining in the pot.	**NEVER distil to dryness** – rapid decomposition of high-boiling impurities could start a fire or explosion. When most of the liquid has been distilled, the temperature may drop somewhat, due to insufficient volatile material remaining to bathe the thermometer.
	Consult the End-of-Lab Checklist on the next page for discarding residues.
	At the end of the lab period, be sure to submit all carbon copies, even if you have a notebook page only partially completed. Continue on a fresh page next time.
6) On the due date, submit to your TA the completed report form (p. 93).	

[Consult the End-of-Lab Checklist on the next page for storing product and discarding residues.]

End-of-Lab Checklist

Save	Discard
Keep any foil that you used for insulation.	Discard the liquid samples into the *LIQUID WASTE* container

CHE 327   SIMPLE DISTILLATION RESULT FORM   2017-2018

Student's name_____   **TA's name**_____

Grade_____

On this and all reports, keep your answers succinct (20-30 words). Excessively wordy answers that do not express the ideas clearly will not receive full credit.

1. Fill in the table below based on your data collected during the *Simple Distillation* experiment.

Volume of Distillate (mL)	2	4	6	8	10	12	14
T_{head} (^{o}C)							

(continued)

Volume of Distillate (mL)	16	18	20	22	24	26	28
T_{head} (^{o}C)							

2. a) In the space below, plot your data with the volume of distillate as the horizontal axis and head temperature (T_{head}) as the vertical axis. Draw a **smooth curve** through the points plotted.

b) Clearly indicate the following by placing the corresponding letter on the distillation curve above and use brackets to specify where each fraction begins and ends:

   A. Fraction of the distillate composed mostly of ethanol.
   B. Fraction of the distillate composed mostly of water.
   C. Fraction of the distillate containing a mixture of ethanol and water.

c) The estimated amount of 95% ethanol collected is _____ mL.

d) The estimated amount of water collected is _____ mL.

Experiment 2   CRYSTALLIZATION OF BENZOIC ACID

Benzoic Acid

Benzoic acid, as well as its salts (known as benzoates), is a widely used food preservative due to its ability to prevent the growth of bacteria, yeasts, and mold. It is considered one of the safest food additives. It is also an important precursor in the synthesis of many organic compounds.

In this experiment, you will purify benzoic acid by the technique of crystallization as classically done on a large scale. The technique is effective in removing both soluble and insoluble impurities. Therefore, you should have no trouble removing the small percent of impurities that is present in your sample of crude benzoic acid.

Background Reading

Read Chapter 7 about the crystallization technique, and the Appendix about percent recovery.   Also review "steam bath" in section 3.3.

Webpage Demonstration

View the PowerPoint demonstration about hot filtration and vacuum filtration.

Properties of New Materials

Name	Appearance	Properties	Hazard Statements
Benzoic acid	White solid	Melting point 122 $^\circ$C	May be harmful if swallowed; may cause eye damage, respiratory irritation.
Petroleum ether	Colorless liquid	Boiling point 80-110 $^\circ$C	Flammable May be fatal; may cause drowsiness or dizziness.
95% Ethanol	Colorless liquid	Boiling point 78 $^\circ$C	Flammable Skin and eye irritation

Experimental Procedure

Part A Solvent Trials

Step in procedure	Comments
1) In the following steps, test the solubility of benzoic acid in petroleum ether, water, and 95% ethanol.	Pure benzoic acid, instead of the impure sample, is used for the solvent trial so that any undissolved benzoic acid benzoic acid will not be confused with insoluble impurities.

Solvents are listed in order of increasing polarity. A solid tends to dissolve more readily in a solvent whose polarity is similar to its own. To appreciate this relationship, compare the structures of benzoic acid and the three solvents.

For recording data from multiple trials in your notebook, it is recommended that you draw up a table as part of your pre-lab. Be sure to leave enough space for in-lab observations.

Solvent	Solubility		
	Room Temperature	Boiling	Cold
Petroleum ether			
95% Ethanol			
Water			

a) Put the tip of a spatulaful (about 30 mg) of pure benzoic acid into each of three small test tubes. Add about 1 mL of a different solvent to each test tube.

Test tubes should be completely clean and dry before you perform the solvent tests.

Label the tubes with grease pencil designations. Form the habit of labeling all containers of materials to avoid mix-ups.

b) Mix the contents of each test tube.

The best way to mix contents in a test tube is to hold it at its rim between your fingers and tap it at its bottom.

c) Observe which tubes still contain undissolved benzoic acid; add a boiling stick and heat these samples gently by passing back and forth into a hot water bath.

Whenever you heat a liquid phase, use a boiling aid (a stick or a stone). A stick is recommended here (some stones are too large for a small test tube) and the same boiling stick can be reused. Add a fresh one whenever the liquid is allowed to cool and then reheated. If you forget the boiling aid and start to heat the liquid, let it cool slightly before adding. Otherwise, the liquid may erupt violently from the flask when the addition is made.

To avoid a steam burn, use a test tube holder. To avoid the inhalation of solvent vapor escaping from the test tube, **do not point the test tube toward anybody!**

d) If benzoic acid goes into solution when heated in a particular solvent, plunge that tube into ice and see if a precipitate or crystals form.

2) Identify the most suitable crystallization solvent.

The object is for the solvent to dissolve the material warm and not dissolve it cold. If these criteria cannot be met, you may be using an unsuitable ratio of solvent to benzoic acid. Try a larger ratio (more solvent) if the benzoic acid is too insoluble, a smaller ratio if too soluble.

Part B Large-Scale Crystallization of Benzoic Acid

Step in procedure

Comments

1) Measure 0.4 g crude benzoic acid.

Watch significant figures: 0.4 g means any value from 0.35 g to 0.44 g is acceptable. However, you should weigh your sample accurately to three decimal places as the balance reads.

2) Place the crude benzoic acid into a 50 mL Erlenmeyer flask.

An Erlenmeyer flask is appropriate for operations where it is important to minimize escape of vapors and to mix vigorously by swirling. If the flask is too big, you will lose material by spreading it out over the surface of the glass.

3) Add 10 mL of the chosen solvent to the flask and heat the flask on a hot plate.

You need a boiling stick or stone here and also at later heating stages.

Do not use a test tube holder here – it is designed for test tubes and may slip out.

4) In a second Erlenmeyer flask, preheat about 20 mL of the chosen solvent on the hot plate. Keep this warm until step 8 is completed.

5) Set up the apparatus for hot filtration, described here and shown on the webpage: Put 5 mL of the chosen crystallization solvent in a 50 mL beaker. Place a stemless funnel with fluted filter paper on top. Preheat the apparatus on the hot plate, and keep it warm until step 8 is completed.

Review the hot filtration technique in section 7.3.

Use the largest size paper that will nest completely inside the funnel. Your TA will demonstrate how to prepare the fluted filter paper (also shown in section 7.3).

It is a good idea to have a watch glass on top of the hot filtration apparatus to minimize evaporation.

6) Keep heating the mixture from step 3, and swirl every so often until all of the benzoic acid has dissolved.

You should try to work reasonably quickly here and in the next few steps so that you add solvent faster than it evaporates!

At all stages, try to distinguish between undissolved benzoic acid and insoluble impurities. Make the best distinction you can so that you do not add a large excess of solvent in an attempt to dissolve the latter.

7) Add 1-2 mL more solvent beyond the point that all the benzoic acid has dissolved; heat the solution briefly.

During the next few steps in which the solution must be kept hot, some solvent will evaporate. The excess here is to prevent evaporation down to the point that benzoic acid crystals form prematurely (in the filter paper in the next step, along with impurities you are trying to remove). In general, the more volatile the solvent, the more should be added in this pre-filtration step.

8) Remove the watch glass lid and filter the solution in small portions through the hot filtration apparatus. After adding each portion, replace the watch glass.

At first, you will probably need to hold the filter paper down with a spatula flat across the top of the funnel.

Adding in small portions will help minimize precipitation of benzoic acid on your filter paper.

If crystals form on top of or beneath the filter paper – which might happen if the glassware is too cool or the solvent has evaporated – wash them through with as a small amount of warm solvent as possible will do the job. Before doing so, mark the level of solution in the beaker with a grease pencil so that you can evaporate down to near this point after the washing. But if you evaporate off so much that crystals begin to form, add a bit more solvent and reheat.

9) Remove the beaker from the hot plate; cool the solution undisturbed to room temperature.

Slow, undisturbed cooling at this stage gives larger, purer crystals.

Place the beaker on a warm surface, such as a book, to help slow down the cooling process.

Keep the funnel in place to serve as a lid until the solution has cooled to room temperature.

10) After the solution is at equilibrium at room temperature, cool further in an ice-water bath. At this time, also cool 5-10 mL the crystallization solvent to be used in for washing the crystals in step 13.

Make your own small ice-water bath at your bench to avoid an accidental tip-over.

The washing solvent is usually the same as the one used for crystallization.

11) Collect the crystals by vacuum filtration.

The set-up here is the same as shown in Figure 7.3 and also on the webpage.

Because the Buchner funnel is made out of opaque porcelain, there may be an undetectable residue inside. To be safe, clean the funnel well with acetone and then rinse with the crystallization solvent before you use it.

When you break up the crystals with a spatula so that you can transfer them to the Buchner funnel, you should notice that there is still supernatant liquid. This liquid is necessary to keep impurities that were not removed in previous steps in solution. If all the liquid has evaporated, you should add a few milliliters fresh solvent, reheat to re-dissolve, and re-cool to recrystallize.

Solid may form in the filter flask due to evaporation of solvent under vacuum. This solid is less pure than your crystals and should not be combined with them.

12) First break the vacuum and then wash the crystals with several small portions of ice-cold crystallization solvent (try to use a minimum amount); stir gently with a spatula; re-apply suction to remove the excess solvent.

Do not scrape the filter paper with the spatula – fibers might be loosened and mix with the crystals, or the paper might tear.

Be sure you have a strong vacuum so that the excess solvent is pulled through.

13) Allow the crystals to dry in the Buchner funnel.$^{\Sigma}$

Make note of the crystal form (commonly needles or plates).

In this and the following experiments, a stopping point is indicated by a "Σ" sign.

14) Determine the weight and calculate the percent recovery after lab.

Remove the boiling stone before weighing. Read Appendix A about percent recovery.

15) On the due date, submit to your TA the remaining benzoic acid in a tightly closed vial (labeled). Also submit the result form with the information requested.

The label on the benzoic acid product vial will be graded. The following information should be on the label: the date, your name, the name of the material, and the weight of material _in the vial_. The date should be when you actually placed the material into the vial.

[Consult the End-of-Lab Checklist below for storing product and discarding residues.]

End-of-Lab Checklist

Save	Discard
Lab period 1 (up to Part B step 13):	**Lab period 1 (up to Part B step 13):**
From Part B step 13: Let the benzoic acid crystals dry in the Buchner funnel.	1) The mixtures from the small test tubes in the solvent trials go into either the _LIQUID WASTE_ or the _SOLID WASTE_ container, as appropriate.
	2) Scrape the solids off the fluted filter paper from the hot filtration. If there is a substantial amount of benzoic acid here, you probably want to hold onto it until you determine your percent recovery. If there is really very little useful solid here, discard the remains in the _SOLID WASTE_ container.
	3) The scraped fluted filter paper goes into the _SOLID WASTE_ container.
	4) If you have any unused petroleum ether or 95% ethanol, it goes into the _LIQUID WASTE_ container. In the future, to avoid waste, try to estimate more carefully the amount of solvent (or reagent) you will need.
Lab period 2 (Part B steps 14 & 15):	**Lab period 2 (Part B steps 14 & 15):**
1) From Part B step 14: Transfer the benzoic acid to the vial in which you will be submitting it for grading. Check to be sure that the label contains all the required information – this is detailed in Part C step 16 and applies not only here but to later products as well.	1) The filter paper from the Buchner funnel goes into the _SOLID WASTE_ container.
	2) The residues from the supernatant and the hot filtration can be discarded into the _LIQUID WASTE_ and/or _SOLID WASTE_ containers when you have determined that you do not need them.

Post-Lab Study Questions

As usual, consider the purpose of each step in the procedure. In addition:

1. Would any of the solvents tested in Part A be entirely unsuitable for crystallizing benzoic acid? Explain.

2. How would you go about finding a crystallizing solvent for an unknown solid if the procedure you followed in Part A did not produce one?

3. What would you do in each of the following cases?

    a) You noticed a large amount of crystals forming in the fluted filter during hot filtration.

    b) You noticed crystals forming in the beaker after hot filtration, but while the solution was still being heated on the steam bath.

    c) You could see that you did not have many crystals after ice cooling.

    d) You washed the crystals in the Buchner funnel with room temperature solvent and greatly reduced your yield.

4. Where would you predict most of the impurity ends up?

CHE 327   CRYSTALLIZATION RESULT FORM   2017-2018

Student's name_____   **TA's name**_____

Grade_____

Hand in to your TA your benzoic acid in a tightly closed, properly labeled vial along with this sheet.

Fill in:

1. What was the weight of product being submitted **in the vial?** _____

2. What was the percent recovery? _____ Show the work.

3. a) Which solvent was used for crystallization in Part B? _____

    b) In the solubility test in part A, did this solvent dissolve benzoic acid completely when it was boiling? Yes or No (Circle one.)

    c) In the solubility test in part A, did precipitate (or crystallize) form when the benzoic acid solution in this solvent was placed in the ice bath? Yes or No (Circle one.)

(For the use of graders only)

Weight Check_____   Weight Grade _____

Yield <u>OK</u>   LOW   <u>REFILL/NO PRODUCT</u>   Yield Grade _____

Appearance <u>GOOD</u>   OK   POOR   Purity Grade _____

                                                     Label _____

Experiment 3   TRIMYRISTIN FROM NUTMEG

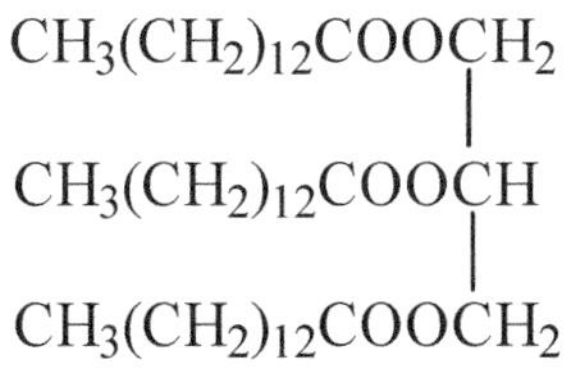

$$CH_3(CH_2)_{12}COOCH_2$$
$$|$$
$$CH_3(CH_2)_{12}COOCH$$
$$|$$
$$CH_3(CH_2)_{12}COOCH_2$$

Trimyristin

In this experiment, you will isolate a single compound, trimyristin, from among the complicated mixture of natural products in its source, nutmeg.

The procedure is designed to separate trimyristin from contaminants and improve its purity. As you work on this experiment, think how each step contributes to an overall goal.

Here is a brief summary of the *Trimyristin* experiment:

1) The ground nutmeg is treated with the solvent ether. The solution containing trimyristin is filtered so as to remove the insoluble plant material. The solvent is evaporated, leaving a residue of crude trimyristin.

2) The crude trimyristin is dissolved in the hot solvent acetone. When the solution is cooled, the trimyristin crystallizes out, leaving in solution the majority of the (colored) impurities.

Background Reading

Review the theory, the general procedure, the related technique (rotary evaporation) of extraction in sections 9.2 and 9.5, and Chapter 8 about melting point.

Properties of New Materials

Name	Appearance	Properties	Hazard Statements
Trimyristin	Colorless solid	Melting point 56 °C	--------
Diethyl ether (ether)	Colorless liquid	Boiling point 35 °C	Highly flammable and mildly toxic
			May cause drowsiness and dizziness, skin and eye irritation
Acetone	Colorless liquid	Boiling point 56 °C	Highly flammable and mildly toxic
			May cause drowsiness and dizziness, mild skin and eye irritation

Experimental Procedure

Part A Extraction

Step in procedure	Comments
1) Weigh out 4.0 g ground nutmeg.	Watch significant figures.
2) Transfer the nutmeg to a 50 mL Erlenmeyer flask.	
3) Measure 25 mL ether by pouring into a graduated cylinder.	The term "ether" can be confusing because there is more than one kind. When used alone, the term means "diethyl ether."
	The pipet provided on the solvent bottle is for a transfer of a small or exact amount and need not be used here.
4) Add the ether to the nutmeg. Swirl the mixture often over a period of about 15 minutes while you set up for the filtration in step 6.	This step extracts most of the trimyristin from the nutmeg into the ether. You should gently cover the flask with a cork in between swirling to minimize evaporation.
5) Pre-weigh a 100 mL rbf and clamp it to a ring stand. Set into the rbf a stemless funnel with a fluted fast-flow filter paper.	Fast-flow filter paper will be distributed by the TA. You should use an iron ring to support the stemless funnel.
6) Perform a gravity filtration by transferring the solution in one of two ways: by pipetting it through the filter into the flask; or by pouring it "smartly," that is, quickly and carefully so that it does not dribble down the outside of the glassware.	Gravity filtration is used when you want to keep the liquid. The setup is the same as that of hot filtration. Good judgment and technique here (and in step 7) are necessary to avoid major loss of product. If filtration is not rapid, so much ether may evaporate that the desired product will be deposited on top of the paper instead of passing through in solution. Be sure to pay attention to the following:
	a) To avoid clogging the pores of the filter paper, try to keep most of the solids in the Erlenmeyer flask while you transfer the solution.
	b) In between solution transfers, a small watch glass (a large one will make the apparatus unstable) on top of the funnel can serve to hold the filter paper down and minimize solvent evaporation.

7) Wash the residue in the Erlenmeyer flask several times with a pipetful of fresh ether, no more than a few mL in all. Filter each wash into the rbf.

If a crust of white solids is observed on any of the glassware or in or under the filter paper, use some of the ether to dissolve it and filter it into the bulk of the solution.

Step 7 completes the extraction.

8) Remove the solvent using the rotary evaporator (rotovap).

Watch a demonstration on how to use a rotovap (more detailed instructions are given in section 9.5). Be sure the trap directly above the rbf is reasonably clean in case you need to recover some of your product from it.

In this experiment, the water bath should be at room temperature. If warm, the ether may boil too vigorously and expel solid from the flask into the trap.

The crude trimyristin will be either a solid or mushy semi-solid. Stop evaporation at the point when only solid remains or when the appearance of the semi-solid has not changed over several minutes.

To stop the rotary evaporation, open the clamp at the T-tube to let the air in first to prevent water backup; then turn off the water.

9) Weigh your rbf and determine the weight of your crude product.

Either during or after class, determine the percent recovery of crude trimyristin from nutmeg.

10) In a small test tube, save a very small amount of crude product (a few milligrams) for melting point, and proceed with the rest of the material to Part B.

Part B Small Scale Crystallization of Trimyristin

Step in procedure	Comments

1) Set up a water bath in a large beaker and place it on a hot plate. Begin heating the water bath.

You will share the water bath with one other student. The water bath will not need to reach boiling temperature. A warm water bath will be sufficient for this experiment.

2) Add 5 mL acetone to the rbf containing the crude trimyristin.

3) Heat the rbf gently in the water bath and swirl until all the solid has dissolved. Immersing only the bottom half of the rbf will be sufficient in heating the solution.

The appropriate amount of solvent for a given weight of solid will vary with the system. Usually it is determined by adding small portions of solvent and boiling until the solid just dissolves (the saturation point). In this experiment, the amount has been predetermined for you. However, if 5 mL acetone is insufficient to dissolve all of your trimyristin, add a little more until complete dissolution is achieved. However, do not exceed more than 10 mL acetone total.

4) Quickly pipet the hot solution into a large test tube.

5) Rinse the rbf with a small amount of acetone; heat; and add the hot rinse to the test tube.

6) Add a boiling stick to the test tube and mix the contents. If the total volume is more than half of the test tube, heat the test tube gently to boil off some of the acetone.

Use a test tube holder to hold the test tube when heating. You should only dip the very bottom of the test tube into the water bath to heat the solution. Pay careful attention during heating, as the solution can boil suddenly and spill out of the test tube. You may need to remove the test tube from the water bath from time to time.

7) Remove the boiling stick and allow the solution to cool to room temperature undisturbed and then to ice temperature.

8) Obtain an unchipped pipet. Squeeze the air out of the bulb and carefully press the tip of the pipet flat to the bottom of the test tube. Then release the bulb to remove the supernatant solution by drawing it into the pipet. Repeat until all of the solvent has been removed.

If done properly, the supernatant will slowly be drawn up into the pipet, leaving the crystals in the test tube.

To avoid sucking up crystals, do not raise the pipet until the bulb fills with air.

9) Add enough ice-cold acetone (pre-chilled in an ice-water bath) to the test tube so that all the solid is immersed in the cold solvent.

10) Remove the wash solvent by pipet using the same technique as in step 8.

You may decide to repeat this wash step, even more than once, if it noticeably improves the appearance of your product. However, keep in mind that too much (and too warm) wash solvent will dissolve away your product. Good judgment and technique here lead to high-quality product.

11) Leave the test tube open over the week for the product to dry.[Σ]

You can try gently tapping the test tube on its side to spread out the solid along the walls of the test tube. Increasing the surface area here will help the drying process.

12) Weigh the dry purified product.

Determine the percent recovery of crystallized trimyristin from crude and that of crystallized trimyristin from nutmeg.

13) In two capillary tubes, simultaneously determine the melting points of the crude and crystallized trimyristin.

If the impure material is too gummy to get into a capillary tube, you will have to omit taking its melting point.

How to determine a melting point and report it is discussed in section 8.2.

Keep in mind that the thermometer may have an error estimated to be as much as ± 5 °C below about 150 °C and slightly greater as the temperature increases. A compound is considered acceptably pure if it melts within this error margin of the literature with a range spanning 2 °C or less.

14) Save some of your crystallized product for another melting point experiment during the *Myristic Acid* experiment. On the due date, submit to your TA the remaining trimyristin in a tightly closed and properly labelled vial, along with the completed result form.

End-of-Lab Checklist

Save	Clean	Discard
1) From Part A step 10: Save a few milligrams crude trimyristin in a labeled test tube for melting point. 2) From Part B step 11: Leave your trimyristin in the Buchner funnel (labeled).	Clean the glassware that contained trimyristin with a brush and soapy water. You will need to scrub well to remove the oily residue.	1) From Part A: Even though it is a food substance, the insoluble nutmeg residue MUST go into the *SOLID WASTE* container since it was contaminated with ether. For the same reason, in this experiment the filter paper and paper towels MUST also go into the *SOLID WASTE* container. 2) The acetone filtrate from Part B step 8 will eventually go into the *LIQUID WASTE* container. However, if you wish to hold onto this material for the time being, you may store it in a test tube, either corked or open.

Post-Lab Study Questions

1. While pouring the ether solution through the filter paper, a crust of white solid is often observed on the glassware. What is this solid, and how did it get there?

2. How might you be able to tell if washing crystals has been effective?

3. What do the melting points of crude and crystallized trimyristin tell you about the purity of these two samples? Consider range as well as value.

4. Recoveries in general are not 100% for both theoretical and practical reasons. Discuss, and relate to your own experiment.

5. If you have a compound whose literature melting point you don't know, how can the experimentally determined melting point provide evidence of purity?

CHE 327   TRIMYRISTIN RESULT FORM   2017-2018

Student's name_____   **TA's name**_____

Grade_____

Hand in to your TA your trimyristin in a tightly closed, properly labeled vial along with this sheet.

Fill in:

1. What was the weight of product being **submitted in the vial?** _____

2. What was the observed melting point range of product being submitted? _____
    Considering ONLY the melting point data, is your product pure or impure? _____

3. What was the percent recovery of your <u>purified</u> trimyristin (from Part B step 12) based on the amount of crude trimyristin you obtained (from Part A step 9)?_____ Show the work.

(For the use of graders only)

Weight Check_____   Weight Grade _____

Yield <u>OK</u>   LOW   <u>REFILL/NO PRODUCT</u>   Yield Grade _____

Appearance <u>GOOD</u>   OK   POOR   Purity Grade _____

MP _____   Label _____

111

Experiment 4   MYRISTIC ACID FROM TRIMYRISTIN

In this experiment, you will convert trimyristin by alkaline hydrolysis to the potassium salt of myristic acid. Both this salt and glycerol, the other product, are soluble in the reaction solvent. When the solution is acidified, the myristic acid is obtained in solid form.

$$CH_2OOC(CH_2)_{12}CH_3$$
$$|$$
$$CHOOC(CH_2)_{12}CH_3 \quad + \quad 3\ KOH \quad \xrightarrow[\text{heat}]{CH_3CH_2OH/H_2O} \quad CHOH \quad + \quad 3\ CH_3(CH_2)_{12}COO^-K^+$$
$$|$$
$$CH_2OOC(CH_2)_{12}CH_3$$

Trimyristin

CH_2OH
$|$
$CHOH$
$|$
CH_2OH

Glycerol   Potassium myristate
(soluble)   (soluble)

$$CH_3(CH_2)_{12}COO^-K^+ \quad + \quad HCl \quad \xrightarrow{H_2O} \quad CH_3(CH_2)_{12}COOH \quad + \quad KCl$$

Myristate acid
(precipitate)   (soluble)

Background Reading

Read Chapter 10 about reflux and the Appendix about percent yield and theoretical yield.

Webpage Demonstration

View the PowerPoint demonstration about reflux.

Properties of New Materials*

Name	Appearance	Melting Point ($^{\circ}$C)	Comments
Myristic acid	White solid	54	May cause eye irritation
Potassium hydroxide	White solid	361	Corrosive even when dilute; may cause severe skin burns and eye damage; harmful if swallowed.
Hydrochloric acid	Colorless gas or aqueous solution	--------	Corrosive even when dilute; may cause severe skin burns, eye damage, and respiratory irritation.
Ligroin	Colorless liquid	--------	Flammable; may be fatal if swallowed; may cause genetic defects and cancer

Safety Precautions

- As always, avoid contact with the chemicals. If you spill the acid or base on your skin, wash immediately and thoroughly with cold running water, and notify your instructor. Always follow the specified order of addition of reagents to a container.

- When heating with a heating mantle, do not put aluminum foil under the flask – this causes overheating, which is a fire hazard.

- Never heat a closed system – it could explode! Leave the top of the condenser open.

Pre-Lab Study Questions

1. At approximately what temperature will the synthesis be carried out? How will this temperature be maintained?

2. Why is it important to acidify the basic solution obtained from reflux completely?

3. Under what circumstance would the procedure in Part B give you material that are no purer than originally?

Experimental Procedure

Part A Synthesis

Step in procedure

1) Divide your trimyristin product as following:

```
                    ┌─────────────┐
                    │ Trimyristin │
                    └─────────────┘
                  ↙                 ↘
   ┌──────────────────┐    ┌──────────────────┐
   │ Use 0.15 g for   │    │ Submit the rest  │
   │ this experiment. │    │ for grading.     │
   └──────────────────┘    └──────────────────┘
        ↙            ↘
┌──────────────────┐  ┌──────────────────┐
│ Keep about 10 mg │  │ Transfer the rest│
│ for mixed melting│  │ to a small rbf.  │
│ points in Part C │  │                  │
└──────────────────┘  └──────────────────┘
```

2) Transfer the trimyristin to a 10 mL rbf.

3) Clamp the rbf to a ring stand 10-15 cm above bench height.

4) Using a funnel, add 5 mL 5.0% potassium hydroxide in 95% ethyl alcohol.

5) Swirl to mix, and add a boiling stone.

6) Attach a condenser to the flask.

Comments

Be sure to set the MP sample aside <u>now,</u> separately from the trimyristin you will be submitting for grading.

The amount needed for MP measurement is small (~10 mg) and the weight of trimyristin being used for the synthesis will not be affected significantly. Therefore, <u>you do not need to weigh it again after setting aside the 10 mg trimyristin for Part C.</u> When you calculate the percent yield of the myristic acid, use 0.15 g as the amount used.

The basic solution has been prepared for you and contains 0.050 g potassium hydroxide per milliliter.

The solvent itself is a mixture of 95% ethyl alcohol (ethanol) and 5% water. This is the common form of lab ethyl alcohol, which cannot be freed of water by simple means.

Potassium hydroxide is corrosive even when dilute. Wear heavy-duty gloves when poring the solution.

The setup is shown in Figure 10.1 and on the webpage.

Be sure to grease the ground glass joint evenly and thoroughly to allow you to disassemble your apparatus later. "Freezing" of joints is a particular problem with hot alkaline solutions. But be moderate – you don't want an excess of grease that will contaminate your product.

7) In the same way as you did in the *Simple Distillation* experiment, connect hoses (water inlet at the bottom).

8) Turn on the water faucet nearest your bench and adjust the flow to a gentle stream.

Too high a water pressure can force the hoses off in step 7, causing a flood.

9) Support a heating mantle of proper size on a ring and fit the mantle as snugly as possible to the flask.

Ideally, the fit should be tight all around. Keep in mind that a heating mantle of a designated size is not designed to fit a flask of larger size. However, it can be used for smaller flasks – fill the space between flask and mantle with a collar of aluminum foil. **Do not put the foil under the flask – this causes overheating, which is a fire hazard.**

10) Plug the heating mantle into a Variac; the switch should be in the off position.

11) Turn on the Variac and reflux for one hour.

Adjust the voltage so as to achieve gentle boiling; try 50-60 V (or 15-20 %). Once the reflux is stable, you may leave the area to do lab work elsewhere, for example melting points. However, you should request another student to keep an eye on your reaction. **Never leave a system that is reacting or being heated unattended.**

Bench work that may be done during the reflux period includes preparation of the hydrochloric acid solution (step 13) and setting up the vacuum filtration apparatus (step 15).

12) Remove the heating mantle but keep the condenser in place until the solution has cooled to lukewarm or room temperature.

Retaining the condenser while the solution cools keeps the amount of escaping vapors to a minimum. After several minutes, you may bring up a room temperature water bath from underneath to immerse the flask and speed up the cooling process.

13) In a 50 mL beaker, chill 5 mL 1 M hydrochloric acid.

The acid solution has been prepared for you and contains 1 mole of hydrochloric acid per liter.

Hydrochloric acid is corrosive even when dilute. Wear heavy-duty gloves when poring the solution.

14) Slowly pour the solution from step 12 into the cold acid and stir vigorously for a few minutes.

To be sure acidification has been accomplished, test the pH with litmus paper.

15) Dilute the solution with 5 mL cold water and collect the solid by vacuum filtration.

The setup here is the same as in the *Benzoic acid* experiment, and also on the webpage.

16) Wash the surface of the product with several small portions of cold water and suck air through for about 15 minutes.

Part B Purification

<u>Step in procedure</u>

<u>Comments</u>

1) Place most of the myristic acid from Part A in a large test tube.

Save about 15 mg of this crude myristic acid for melting point measurement in step 9.

2) Add 3 mL ligroin.

The myristic acid should dissolve. Examine closely – <u>if there is a water droplet, or an aqueous layer, remove it using a pippet</u>.

3) Pre-weigh a clean large test tube and set it aside for use in step 5.

4) Prepare a filter pipet for use in step 5:

   a) With a boiling stick, push a small wad of cotton down into the top of the stem of a pipet.

   The cotton should be pushed into the opening firmly but not tightly packed.

   b) Scoop up Celite into the pipet. Tap the bottom of the pipet against the bench top, covered with some form of padding – your notebook would be suitable. Add enough Celite until you obtain a height of about 1 cm.

   Celite is diatomaceous earth that serves as a filter aid.

5) With a second pipet, transfer a portion of the myristic acid solution into the filter pipet, the tip of which should be resting in the large test tube from step 3.

Support the flask by resting it in a beaker or by holding it.

6) Attach a rubber bulb to the top of the filter pipet and gently force the liquid through into the large test tube. Repeat steps 5 and 6 until all the liquid has been filtered through.

After use, discard the filter pipet and its solid contents in the glass waste box.

7) Leave the large test tube open until the next period to let the solvent evaporate.$^{\Sigma}$

If you omitted steps 3-6, your product will be in a test tube at this point; leave the tube open so that you recover the crude product after a week's evaporation.

If you performed steps 3-6 to remove insoluble impurities, the product here should be purer than the crude from Part A.

8) Weigh the dry product.

After class, determine the percent yield of purified myristic acid from trimyristin – read about percent yield in the Appendix.

Part C Mixed Melting Point

Although the term "mixed melting point" is widely used, there are some who prefer the more accurately descriptive "mixture melting point."

<u>Step in procedure</u>

<u>Comments</u>

1) In three capillary tubes, simultaneously take the melting points of your purified myristic acid, trimyristin, and a well-mixed 1:1 mixture of the two.

For the 1:1 mixture, use your spatula to chop, stir, and mash the two samples together on a watch glass. Obviously very little material will be needed.

2) Record the data and interpret carefully.

In the reaction of trimyristin to myristic acid, starting material and product have essentially the same melting point. Therefore, obtaining the expected value for myristic acid gives no evidence one way or the other as to whether reaction has occurred. Such evidence, however, may be obtained by the mixed melting point technique.

End-of-Lab Checklist

Save	Discard
1) From the *Trimyristin* experiment Part B step 14: Transfer the trimyristin to the vial in which you will be submitting it for grading.	1) The acidified aqueous solution, which was in your filter flask and contains glycerol and salts, goes into the *LIQUID WASTE* container.
2) From the *Myristic Acid* experiment Part B step 8: Save purified myristic acid for melting point in Part C.	2) The filter paper from the Buchner funnel goes into the *SOLID WASTE* container.
3) If you used aluminum foil for the heating mantle, save it in case you need it in the future.	3) The filter pipet that contains Celite goes into the *GLASS* waste box.

Post-Lab Study Questions

1. What percent yield did you obtain for myristic acid? Give reasons why the value was not 100%.

2. What information do you get from measuring two or three melting points simultaneously that you do not get from measuring them sequentially?

3. What were your mixed melting point data, and how should they be interpreted? What is the reasoning behind the mixed melting point technique?

Experiment 5

A THIN LAYER CHROMATOGRAPHY STUDY OF BROMINE-CATALYZED ISOMERIZATION OF DIMETHYL MALEATE TO DIMETHYL FUMARATE

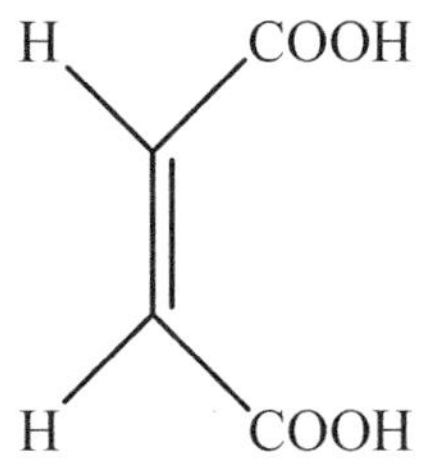

Maleic Acid
(*cis*-Butenedioic Acid)

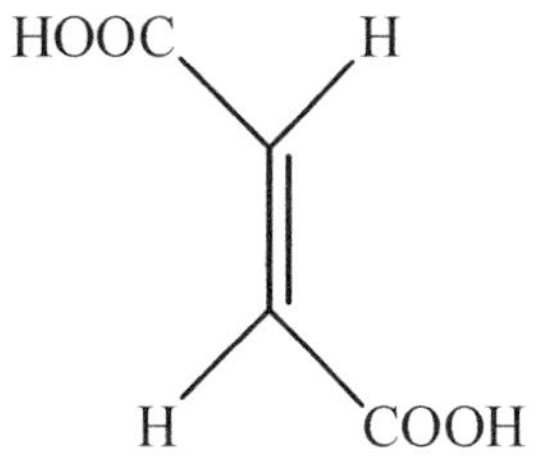

Fumaric Acid
(*trans*-Butenedioic Acid)

In the presence of light and with bromine catalysis, the methyl ester of maleic acid, dimethyl maleate, can be converted to the methyl ester of fumaric acid, dimethyl fumarate. This reaction was the first example of *cis-trans* alkene isomerization to be studied in detail.

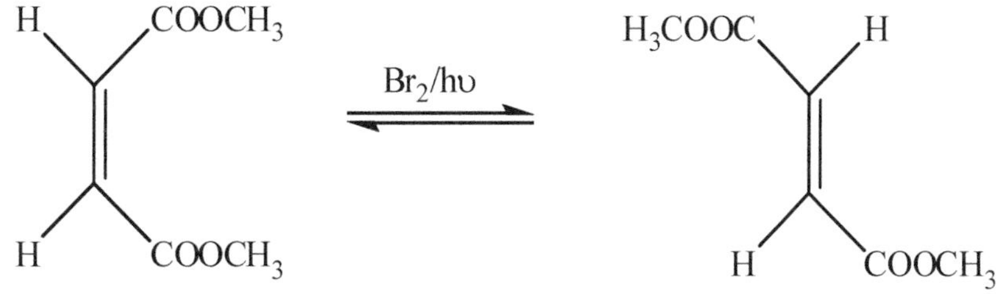

Dimethyl Maleate
MW = 144   d = 1.15 g/mL
mp = -19 °C   soluble in cold CH_2Cl_2

Dimethyl Fumarate
MW = ?   mp = 101-102 °C

In this experiment, you will use thin layer chromatography (TLC) to monitor the above reaction. It is used routinely in organic chemistry to follow the course of a reaction: the disappearance of reactant(s) and the appearance of product(s), that is, the change of the composition of the reactant/product mixture. At the beginning of this isomerization reaction, only dimethyl maleate is present; as the reaction proceeds, dimethyl fumarate accumulates as its precursor diminishes. Since this isomerization reaction is reversible, there is a question as to whether the final product contains unreacted starting material. You will be able to answer this question by application of the TLC technique.

TLC differentiates compounds by their polarity. Because dimethyl maleate is more polar than dimethyl fumarate, this difference should allow you to detect one compound in the presence of the other and to identify both.

Background Reading

Read section 11.1 for a general introduction to chromatography and section 11.2 for the TLC technique.

Webpage Demonstration

View the PowerPoint demonstration about TLC.

Properties of New Materials*

Name	Appearance	Properties	Comments
Methylene chloride (dichloromethane)	Colorless liquid	Boiling point 40 °C	Halogenated, suspected of causing cancer; may cause drowsiness or dizziness, skin and respiratory irritation, serious eye irritation; may cause damage to organs through prolonged or repeated exposure if swallowed.
Hexanes	Colorless liquid	Boiling point 67-69 °C	Flammable, may cause drowsiness or dizziness, skin and eye irritation; may cause damage to organs through prolonged or repeated exposure if swallowed; suspected of damaging fertility; may be fatal if swallowed.
Ethyl acetate	Colorless liquid	Boiling point 77 °C	Flammable; may cause skin and eye irritation.
Bromine	Red-brown liquid	Boiling point 59 °C	Oxidative and corrosive; may cause severe skin burns and eye damage; may be harmful if swallowed, fatal if inhaled.
Dimethyl maleate	Colorless liquid	Boiling point 204-207 °C	Harmful if swallowed; toxic in contact with skin; may cause skin and respiratory irritation, serious eye irritation; may cause allergic skin reaction.
Dimethyl fumarate	White crystal	Melting point 100-102 °C	Harmful if swallowed; harmful in contact with skin; may cause skin and eye it; may cause allergic skin reaction.
Silica	White solid	--------	May cause eye irritation; excessive inhalation may cause lung disease.

Safety Precautions

- Although bromine (Br_2) is an oxidizer and corrosive, the bromine solution used in this course is diluted and much less harmful. The reaction should be carried out in the fume hood. Wear long sleeves and heavy-duty gloves. Avoid inhaling the vapor. If you spill the bromine solution, inform your instructor **immediately**.

- Methylene chloride, hexanes and ethyl acetate are moderate health hazards. Methylene chloride has for some time been a suspect carcinogen. Hexanes and ethyl acetate are flammable.

- Ultraviolet (UV) light can cause painful burns to eyes, with even a very brief exposure. **Do not look directly at the light source.**

Experimental Procedure

Part A Introduction to TLC Techniques

Step in procedure	**Comments**
1) Obtain the silica plates with fluorescent indicator that you will need for the entire experiment.	You will need a 2 x 6.5 cm plate for Part A, and a larger 5 x 6.5 cm plate for Part B. The plates will be backed by aluminum foil. **Do not touch the adsorbent surface at any time during the experiment** – oils from the skin may contaminate the plates.
2) In Part A of this experiment, work in a group of three students. For the remainder of the experiment, work individually.	Each student in the group will use a different solvent in the chamber in step 3, either hexanes, ethyl acetate, or a 1:1 mixture of hexanes:ethyl acetate. At the end of Part A, you should see the effect that changing the polarity of the solvent has on the TLC results (see step 13). As part of your data, write the full name of the other two students in your notebook, along with which solvent each of you is using.
3) Prepare your TLC chamber by filling it with your solvent to a depth of about ½ cm.	The TLC chamber is a 400 mL beaker with flat rim. The setup is shown in Figure 11.1 in Chapter 11 and also on the webpage.
4) Place a half piece of filter paper around and touching the inside of the chamber.	Give the other half paper to another student. At the end of the period, keep your paper in the chamber for use in later experiments. The filter paper acts as a wick from which solvent evaporates to saturate the air space. The chamber should stand covered for several minutes before use to ensure this process is complete.
5) Obtain a supply of micropipets for spotting the compounds onto the plates. Seven to eight micropipets should be adequate for the entire experiment.	Micropipets will be distributed by your TA or will be available in the stockroom.
6) One centimeter from the short edge of a small plate, make a light pencil mark at the left side, as shown in the drawing in step 7.	This mark defines the origin.

7) Next to the mark, equidistant from each other and the sides, spot the dimethyl fumarate standard at two locations:

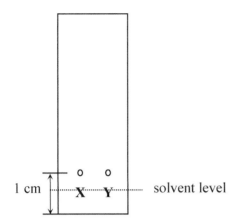

1 cm ⊢·········· X   Y ··········⊣ solvent level

a) At the first location, spot the dimethyl fumarate one time.

b) At the other location, spot the dimethyl fumarate about ten times superimposed.

8) Check the plate under short wavelength UV light.

9) Using forceps, carefully place the TLC plate almost vertically in the development chamber on the side away from the filter paper.

Below each location, lightly write an identifying code letter or number, which you should explain in your notebook. These codes are shown in the example as X and Y.

Do not outline the spots at the origin or scrape into the adsorbent surface with the pencil.

Before spotting with the actual dimethyl fumarate standard, practice spotting using pure solvent (such as hexanes), which will evaporate upon spotting. This allows you to get a feel for how much pressure to apply in order to create a spot that is not too small or too large, without any risk of wasting the silica plate.

Keep the spot small (as shown) by touching the micropipet gently to the silica and lifting immediately. If in spite of your care the spot is too large (as observed under UV light in step 8), you may rotate the plate 180° so that the other end becomes the origin, and try again.

Allow the plate to dry between each of a series of spottings, and at the end before placing in the developing chamber. By spotting lightly and heavily in (a) and (b), you should be able to observe the effect of concentration on the appearance of spots after development (see step 11).

Do not look directly at the UV lamp!

Some materials, such as dimethyl fumarate, are visualized under UV light. For these materials, you can tell if they are present where wanted (at the origin where you spotted), present where unwanted (contaminating the plate at other locations), or absent. You can of course get no information for UV-invisible materials by this method.

If you have measured as instructed, the spots will initially be above the level of the solvent. The plate should not touch any surface along its side; it rests against the glass at the top and bottom.

As development progresses, the solvent will be drawn up the plate by capillary action.

10) When the solvent front has advanced to about ½ cm from the top edge, remove the plate from the development chamber.

If you rotated the plate as described in step 7a, you should not allow the solvent to advance as far as the original spotting position.

Because of quick evaporation, draw a pencil line along the solvent front as you remove the plate from the chamber.

11) After it has dried, examine the plate by short wavelength UV light.

Because compounds may not be stable, it is good practice to examine soon after development.

12) With a pencil, carefully outline the spots.

Draw a careful outline around each spot, not a circle that indicates its general location. Do not make any mark at the origin unless a spot remains there after development. Consult the illustration in Figure 11.2.

Use a dotted outline for faint spots, if any are observed. In your notebook (not on the plate itself – it would be cluttered), record whether spots are fluorescent (bright against the background) or absorbent (dark).

13) For both yourself and the other students in your group, record the information you will need for R_f calculations.

$$R_f = \frac{\text{distance traveled by the compound}}{\text{distance traveled by the solvent}}$$

Measure each distance from the origin.

In lab, record in your notebook either the measurements needed for R_f calculations or an exactly duplicated full-scale drawing of the plate. From such a drawing, you can measure distances later. R_f values may be calculated after lab and are not required to be recorded in your notebook.

For the three trials in your group, differences in R_f values should be observable depending on the polarity of the solvent. If you cannot discern the difference, or if it is not consistent with what you expect, talk to your instructor before you go on with the experiment.

Part B Bromine-Catalyzed Isomerization of Dimethyl Maleate to Dimethyl Fumarate

Step in procedure

Comments

1) Prepare a large TLC plate as shown below. Spot the dimethyl fumarate standard solution at the origin above the "Std" mark.

The long side (6.5 cm) of the plate is vertical.

Other identification codes will be explained in later steps.

To keep the final spots small, do not apply an excess of material here or at the other locations later. Unless you are advised otherwise, spot three times at each location.

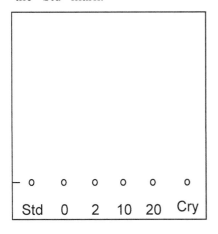

2) Obtain a cork for a 25 mL Erlenmeyer flask and be sure the fit is tight. Add 1 mL dimethyl maleate and 3 mL methylene chloride to the flask. Then immediately cork the flask tightly.

Methylene chloride is very volatile (boiling point at about 40 $^{\circ}$C) and evaporates quickly when left open.

Make sure your flask is completely dry. Any residual acetone will react with bromine during the reaction.

3) On the TLC plate, spot the mixture from step 2 at the origin above mark "0" (see the drawing above).

This corresponds to the reaction mixture at time zero, **before** the reaction begins.

After each spotting, check the plate under UV light to make sure the spot appears in appropriate size and intensity.

4) Move your flask to the hood. Begin the reaction by adding 10 drops of 10% bromine/methylene chloride solution to the mixture. Immediately cork the flask tightly and note the time. Swirl.

Bromine is an oxidizer and corrosive. The reaction should be carried out in the fume hood. Wear long sleeves and heavy-duty gloves and avoid inhaling the vapor. If you spill the bromine solution, inform your instructor immediately.

You may take the corked flask out of the hood so that the contents are exposed to direct light while you swirl.

5) Keep track of the time. Two minutes after you added the bromine solution, **in the hood**, briefly remove the cork so that you can insert a micropipet into the reaction mixture to withdraw a small amount of it. Immediately replace the cork.

6) On the TLC plate, spot the mixture from step 5 at the origin above mark "2" (see the drawing in step 2).

This is the reaction mixture at 2 minutes reaction time.

7) Continue to swirl the flask frequently. At 10 minutes and 20 minutes from the time the bromine solution was added, repeat the procedure in steps 5-6 to apply spots above marks "10" and "20", respectively.

If the reaction mixture completely decolorizes during the reaction period, add a few more drops of 10% bromine solution.

During the reaction period, cool 6-7 mL hexanes in an ice-water bath for use in step 9.

8) At the end of the 20-minute period, cool the reaction mixture in an ice-water bath for at least 10 to 15 minutes.

Temperature plays a crucial role in the formation of crystals in the next step. If the solution is not cold enough, the crystallization will be extremely slow.

9) While swirling the flask gently, add cold hexanes to the mixture dropwise until crystals appear.

Usually about 3-4 mL ice-cold hexanes will be needed for the crystallization.

10) Collect the crystals by vacuum filtration. Wash the crystals with cold hexanes and let them air dry.

11) During the drying period, set up the TLC chamber: Discard the previous solvent and let the chamber air dry for a few minutes; prepare a new developing solvent, a 3:1 hexanes:ethyl acetate mixture; fill the chamber with the new developing solvent to a depth of about ½ cm.

Discard the previous solvent into the *LIQUID WASTE* container.

The chamber does not need to be cleaned, but it must be dried to prevent cross contamination.

About 10-12 mL developing solvent will be needed.

12) Dissolve a few crystals (about 5-10 mg) from step 10 in 1-2 mL methylene chloride. On the TLC plate, spot this solution at the origin above mark "Cry".

Work quickly, as methylene chloride is very volatile – you may need to add a few more drops at some point. Because the solution is dilute, multiple spotting is necessary (see Part A step 7). Check under UV light after spotting 3 or 4 times to see if more is needed.

13) Develop the TLC plate and visualize the spots.

Record the appearance of the spots and their position relative to the origin and solvent front.

At this point, you should be able to identify the compound collected in step 10.

Save this TLC plate. On the due date, submit the result form with the TLC plate attached.

14) On the due date, submit to your TA the TLC plate from step 13 along with the completed result form.

The unused crystals may be recycled.

End-of-Lab Checklist

Save	Discard
1) Keep the filter paper in the TLC chamber for future experiments.	1) The used developing solvent goes to the *LIQUIDS WASTE* container.
2) Save all your developed TLC plates until you are sure you have no further use for them. However, if you lose them, there is no problem because you should have the equivalent information (spot and solvent distances or exact drawings) in your notebook. From this information you could reproduce your observations exactly.	2) The filtrate from Part B step 10 and any other mixtures containing methylene chloride go into the *LIQUIDS WASTE* container.
3) Keep your unused TLC plates in their envelope, inside your drawer.	3) Used micropipets go into the *GLASS* discard box on the floor beneath the waste bottles.
4) Ask your TA for a plastic vial in which to store unused micropipets. You may find a vial of leftover micropipets in your drawer. Feel free to use them if they are of good quality.	4) When you are eventually ready to get rid of them, used TLC plates can go into the *SOLID WASTE* container.

Post-Lab Study Questions

1. In Part A, did you observe a significant effect of varying concentration on the appearance of spots after development?

2. In Part A, what was the effect of changing the developing solvent on R_f from hexanes to 1:1 hexanes:ethyl acetate to ethyl acetate? Is this effect consistent with what you would predict from the polarities of the solvents?

3. Inexperienced workers commonly make mistakes in TLC experiments. Give the result in each of the following cases.

   a) In Part B, at marks 0, 2, 10, 20, you spotted each of the reaction mixtures ten times superimposed.

   b) You got a fingerprint on the silica surface of the TLC plate – along one short side – right in the center.

   c) You spotted ½ cm from the bottom edge and immersed the plate in 1 cm depth of solvent.

   d) You forgot to mark the solvent front the moment you removed the plate from the developing chamber.

4. From the TLC results in Part B, answer the following questions:

   a) What is the identity of the compound collected in step 10?

   b) Which compound, dimethyl maleate or dimethyl fumarate, is more strongly adsorbed on the silica TLC plates? Which one gives a larger R_f value? Explain.

   c) How many spot(s) did you observe in each reaction mixture? Identify all spots and describe the relative intensity. Interpret your results.

   d) How many components did you expect to observe in the reaction mixture at the completion of the reaction (20 minutes reaction time)? What would they be? Did your TLC results confirm the expectation? Explain.

5. What is the molecular weight of the product? What is its percent yield?

6. Both TLC and melting point give purity information. Which results would be more sensitive? Which would be more useful? Explain.

CHE 327 TLC RESULT FORM 2017-2018

Student's name______________________________ **TA's name**______________________

Grade_________

Keep your answers succinct (no more than 20 words). Excessively wordy answers that do not express the idea clearly will not receive full credit.

Directly to the right, attach the TLC plate from Part B.

1. Identify (provide compound name(s)) the spot(s) in mixture 0 on your TLC plate. →

2. How many spots did you expect to see in mixture 0? Why?

3. Identify (provide compound name(s)) the spot(s) in mixture 20 on your TLC. Calculate the R_f values of these compounds (make sure you also mention the eluting solvent).

(For the use of graders only)

Quality of TLC Plate:

Solvent Front/Origin	Yes ______ No	Marks at Origin	Yes ______ No
Large/Overlapping Spots	__________	Missing/Extra Spots	__________

Experiment 6

ISOLATION OF β-CAROTENE FROM SPINACH
BY COLUMN CHROMATOGRAPHY

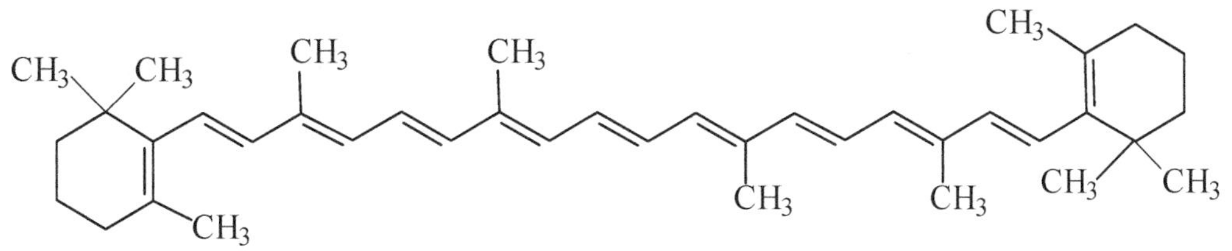

β-Carotene

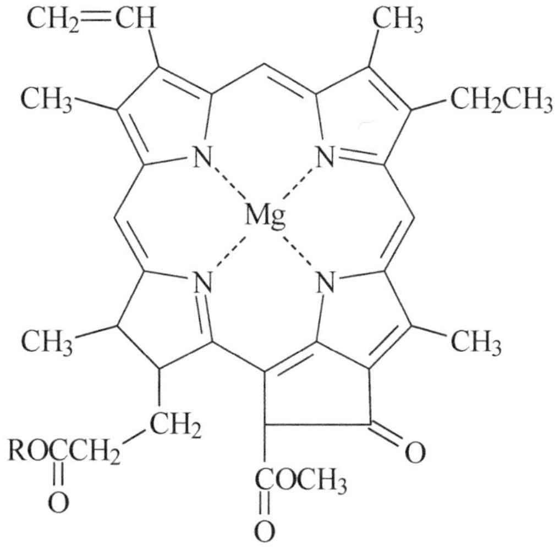

Chlorophyll a

Column chromatography is a scaled-up version of TLC that enables separation of larger samples. In this experiment, you will use the technique to separate β-carotene from among the many pigments (colored substances) found in green plants such as spinach.

Other common green-plant pigments include the chlorophylls (one of which is shown above) and the xanthophylls. Of them all, β-carotene is the least polar.

The experiment consists of several parts:

A) Preparation of the micro-column

B) Extraction of the pigment mixture from spinach, and TLC analysis of the mixture's composition

C) Isolation of β-carotene by column chromatography

D) TLC analysis of column results

Part A (and glassware cleaning for Parts B-D) can be done in a lab session prior to that in which the extraction is performed. Once obtained in solution, the pigments degrade fairly rapidly. Therefore, you should plan to do Parts B-D all in the same period.

Background Reading

Read section 11.3 about column chromatography. Review "Drying Organic Liquids" in section 9.4.

Properties of New Materials

β-Carotene is a bright yellow-orange solid with melting point 178-179 °C. The other pigments are also high-melting solids whose colors range from yellow to orange to green. They are susceptible to decomposition by light and air, as well as heat. All substances should be handled with the usual care.

Experimental Procedure

Part A Preparation of the Micro-Column

Step in procedure	Comments
1) Obtain a short-stemmed pipet for the column.	
2) Using a boiling stick, loosely pack a small piece of cotton into the top of the constriction.	The cotton should not be so tight as to prevent free flow of solvent through the column.
3) Fill the column with silica to a height of 5.5-6 cm.	Use the special funnel provided to transfer the silica to the column. Keep a piece of paper underneath to catch spills. Avoid breathing the silica dust.
4) Pack the silica by tapping the bottom of the column against the bench top, covered with some form of padding – your notebook would be suitable.	This step is finished when the height of the silica shows no further decrease.
5) Carefully insert the top of the column through the hole punched in an orange rubber septum cap.	Watch a demonstration before attempting this step. **Be sure to keep your hands close together as you gently insert the glass tubing with a twisting motion.** Leave about ½ cm glass protruding so that you can apply a rubber bulb later in Part C step 8 if necessary. But position the rubber cap high enough that you can clearly see the top of the silica.

Part B Extraction and TLC of Pigments

You must complete Parts B-D in a single period. You will need about 2 ½ hours, including cleanup time.

Important: All glassware in this experiment must be free of stopcock grease.

Step in procedure	**Comments**
1) Weigh out 2.0 g chopped frozen spinach (thawed) and transfer it to a small Erlenmeyer flask.	**Press it firmly in a paper towel to remove as much water as possible.** Do not waste towels – one is sufficient.
2) Add 15 mL ethyl acetate. With your spatula mash, press, and stir the spinach mixture for about 5-7 minutes.	You need to be vigorous to extract the pigments from the spinach, but don't poke a hole in the flask!
3) Pipet or decant the solution into a second small Erlenmeyer flask. Dry twice with anhydrous sodium sulfate.	Pour enough drying agent into the flask to cover the bottom with a thin layer. Swirl for several minutes and let stand for several minutes more – about five minutes in all. Decant the solution into a third small Erlenmeyer flask and repeat the entire procedure with fresh sodium sulfate. At the end, some of the drying agent should flow like sand, although a portion may be gummy or completely lumped up.
4) Decant the solution into a 25 mL round bottom flask.	Use a funnel to transfer the solution.
	If some of the sodium sulfate gets into the rbf, it is ok since you will only add the dissolved material onto the column in Part C step 6.
5) Rotary evaporate off the solvent.	Use a warm water bath to aid in the evaporation of the ethyl acetate, but do not make it so hot that the pigments will cook.
	The pigments, ready to use for chromatography, will be referred to in the following text as PG. They are susceptible to decomposition by light and air (as well as heat). From this point on, keep all spinach extract in closed containers (sealed with Para-film or corked – make sure the cork fits well before dropping it) in your drawer as much as possible.
6) Dissolve the PG in about 5-6 drops 1:1 ligroin:ethyl acetate.	Prepare 12 mL of the solvent mixture. Use 5-6 drops here and the rest for the TLC chamber in step 8 or for the solutions in Part D step 1.

7) With micropipets, apply the PG and β-carotene solutions next to each other on a 2 x 6.5 cm silica plate.	The stock solution of β-carotene in ethyl acetate has been prepared for you.

Both PG and β-carotene spots should appear strongly colored at this stage so that they will remain visible after development. For the PG solution, about 10 overspottings are recommended, although of course the amount being transferred will depend on the concentration and the size of the pipet opening. Be sure to allow the plate to dry between each application of material.

This step uses only a small portion of the pigments; most of the PG should be saved for Parts C and D. |
8) Develop the plate in 1:1 ligroin:ethyl acetate.	Before putting the plate in the chamber, be sure the spots from step 7 are quite dry; a wait of 1-2 minutes after the last application is a good idea.
9) Carefully outline all spots; record colors immediately after development; record all additional appropriate TLC information as in the previous experiment.	The colors fade very quickly. UV visualization will not be necessary if you outline the spots immediately (and probably will not do any good afterwards!).
10) Keep the TLC chamber for Part D.	

Part C Loading and Running the Column

Pace yourself sensibly. Part D analyzes the results of Part C and must be done the same period. Because you should allow about one hour from the end of the period for Part D (including cleanup), take advantage of the hints in step 8b to speed up the column's progress if necessary.

Step in procedure	Comments
1) Clamp the column vertically by its rubber piece to a ring stand.	The column should be clamped high enough for test tubes to be conveniently introduced and removed underneath. At the same time, it should be low enough that its tip holds the test tubes in place with no additional support.
2) Obtain 15 mL ligroin.	If you are interested in collecting some of the pigments that come after β-carotene (although this is not required), you will need approximately 10 mL of a second eluting solvent, 9:1 ligroin:ethyl acetate. Prepare this now.

3) Pre-number four small test tubes.

The β-carotene may elute in the first or second tube, but it is best to be prepared in case you need additional ones. If you plan to collect some of the later pigments, prepare more than four tubes.

4) Check to be sure the volume of PG solution remains at about 4-5 drops; if necessary, make up to volume with 1:1 ligroin:ethyl acetate solvent.

Perform steps 5-6 within the next 1-2 minutes so that the PG solution doesn't have a chance to dry out significantly.

5) Wet the column with ligroin.

Be sure the entire length of the column is wet. Then let the ligroin run down just to the level of the top of the silica or slightly below.

6) Add <u>most</u> of the PG solution straight down onto the wetted column. Let it run into the silica.

The small amount of PG solution that coats the flask will be used for TLC in Part D of the experiment. Put the flask in your drawer, away from light and air, until you need the PG solution later.

7) Add a few more drops ligroin and let it run down into the column; repeat this wash step until the solvent head above the silica remains colorless (expected to be 1-2 times more).

8) Fill the column with ligroin and begin the run.

   a) Collect the fractions in the test tubes you prepared earlier.

Determine when to switch test tubes by the color of the material being eluted. Keep watch for when the first colored material reaches the bottom of the column, and try to collect it as a separate fraction.

In this experiment, it is not so important to break between colorless and colored materials; but it is important to keep different colors separate.

   b) Keep the column running until the first colored material has been completely eluted.

This step is expected to take no more than ten minutes. If your column is dripping slowly, you should apply air pressure with a rubber bulb. Just hold the bulb in place on top of the column – do not attach it. Squeeze gently to push solvent through, and then raise the bulb before you let air back in.

If you have used about half the ligroin and the first colored band has not moved very far from the top, you may wish to increase the solvent's eluting power. Do this by adding a few drops of ethyl acetate to your ligroin supply (not directly onto the column). When you then switch to this more polar mixed solvent, all the compounds from spinach will elute faster.

138

c) You may wish to continue the experiment to obtain other colored fractions. If so, switch to a more polar solvent after step 8b.

Use the 9:1 ligroin:ethyl acetate solvent you prepared in step 2.

Continue to run the column as long as you wish, but allow an hour to complete Part D and cleanup.

d) In your notebook, be sure to record for each test tube the estimated volume and color (or no color) of solution collected therein.

If you changed the solvent composition at any time, you will need to record this information also.

e) When the experiment is completed, discard the column into the label container in the hood.

9) Transfer the colored fraction from step 8b to a 10 mL rbf and rotary evaporate off the solvent.

Do not spoil the experiment now by using glassware contaminated with water or grease!

If you collected colored fractions other than the one containing β-carotene, you should evaporate off their solvent as well.

Part D TLC Analysis of Results

Step in procedure

1) Dissolve the remaining PG mixture and the colored fraction each in about 3 drops 1:1 ligroin:ethyl acetate.

Comments

If you obtained more than one pigment from the column, you will want to analyze them all by TLC.

2) Under the conditions previously employed, TLC the PG, stock β-carotene, and the colored fraction(s).

Determine whether you were successful in isolating pure β-carotene.

If the R_f value of your β-carotene does not match that of the standard, you may achieve better results by repeating the TLC, taking better care that all spots dry well before development.

End-of-Lab Checklist

Save	Discard
You cannot expect to save useful products from this experiment. It is, as always, important to keep a complete record in your notebook.	1) The used leaves and the towels should go into the *SOLID WASTE* container since they were contaminated with ethyl acetate. 2) The used micropipets go into the *GLASS* container. 3) Add a few milliliters of water to the drying agent; the resulting solution goes into the *LIQUID WASTE* container. All solvents go into the *LIQUID WASTE* container as well.

Post-Lab Study Questions

1. How many pigments could be distinctly seen by TLC in the PG extract? What is your evidence that one of them was β-carotene?

2. Why would you predict β-carotene to be eluted from the column before chlorophyll a?

3. If you obtained other pigments from the column, how might you determine their identity?

CHE 327 β-CAROTENE RESULT FORM 2017-2018

Student's name_______________________________ **TA's name**_______________________

Grade_________

Directly to the right, attach the TLC plate from Part D.

→

(For the use of graders only)

Quality of TLC Plate: ________________________

Separation Quality: ________________________

Based on TLC: GOOD OK POOR

____

Based on lab performance: GOOD OK POOR

Experiment 7   SYNTHESIS OF A FRAGRANT ESTER

Esters are compounds that can be derived from the reaction of a carboxylic acid with an alcohol. Carboxylic esters have the general formula RCOOR', where R and R' may be an alkyl or an aryl group. Naturally occurring esters in fruits and flowers give them their characteristic odors.   For example, 3-methylbutyl ethanoate is artificial banana flavor; and 2-methylpropyl propanoate is characterized in one Internet reference by this odor description: "fruity green ether sweet tutti-frutti banana punch."[1] Esters also perform important functions in the animal. For instance, the ester acetylcholine is a chemical transmitter of nerve stimuli.

In this experiment, you will prepare an ester from a carboxylic acid and an alcohol.

$$RCOOH \ + \ R'OH \ \underset{}{\overset{H_2SO_4}{\rightleftharpoons}} \ RCOOR' \ + \ H_2O$$

To increase the yield of ester in the equilibrium reaction, you may use an excess of one of the reactants, in this case the carboxylic acid. The excess acid left at the end of the reaction is removed by extraction into an aqueous sodium carbonate solution.

$$2 \ RCOOH \ + \ Na_2CO_3 \ \longrightarrow \ 2RCOO^-Na^+ \ + \ CO_2 \ + \ H_2O$$

You will be assigned one of the esters in Table E7.1. The common names of the esters are given in parentheses.

Table E7.1 Properties of esters to be synthesized. [2]

Ester	Boiling Point ($^{\circ}$C)	Density (g/ mL)
Butyl ethanoate (butyl acetate)	126	0.88
3-Methylbutyl ethanoate (isopentyl acetate)	142	0.88
2-Methylpropyl propanoate (isobutyl propionate)	137	0.86
Butyl propanoate (butyl propionate)	145	0.88

As part of the experiment, you must calculate the amounts of carboxylic acid and alcohol you need to use. Be prepared to measure the liquid materials by weight or volume. Molecular weights and densities you will need are listed in Table E7.2.

Table E7.2 Properties of the parent carboxylic acids and alcohols. [3]

Carboxylic Acid	MW (g/mole)	Boiling Point ($^{\circ}$C)	Density (g/ mL)
Acetic acid	60	118	1.05
Propionic acid	74	141	0.99
Alcohol			
Butanol	74	118	0.81
2-Methylpropanol	74	108	0.80
3-Methylbutanol	88	130	0.81

You may wish to check your calculations with a member of the CHE 327 staff. It is most convenient to do this during office hours before the scheduled lab date.

---

[1]http://www.thegoodscentscompany.com/ (accessed 01/2004)
[2,3]http://chemfinder.cambridgesoft.com/ (accessed 01/2004)

Background Reading

1. Lab period 1 (Part A): Read "Acid-Base Extraction" (section 9.3) and review "Drying Organic Liquids" (section 9.4).

2. Lab period 2 (Parts B-D):

   - Review "Simple Distillation" (section 6.3).

   - Read Chapter 12 about infrared (IR) spectroscopy.

   - Read section 11.4 about gas chromatography (GC).

Webpage Demonstration

1. Lab period 1 (Part A): View the PowerPoint demonstration about the use of the separatory funnel.

2. Lab period 2 (Parts B-D): View the PowerPoint demonstration about distillation.

Ester Assignments

There are four different esters to be made in CHE 327. From the chart below, you will find out which ester for you to make using your bench number.

Ester	Bench number			
Butyl ethanoate	1	5	9	13
(butyl acetate)	49	53	57	61
	33	37	41	45
	17	21	25	29
3-Methylbutyl ethanoate	2	6	10	14
(isopentyl acetate)	50	54	58	62
	34	38	42	46
	18	22	26	30
2-Methylpropyl propanoate	3	7	11	15
(isobutyl propionate)	51	55	59	63
	35	39	43	47
	19	23	27	31
Butyl propanoate	4	8	12	16
(butyl propionate)	52	56	60	64
	36	40	44	48
	20	24	28	32

Hazard Statements of New Materials

All materials in this experiment are colorless; all are liquids except anhydrous magnesium sulfate. Physical properties of the carboxylic acids, alcohols, and esters are given in Tables E7.1 and E7.2.

Name	Hazard Statements
Acetic acid	Flammable; may causes severe skin burns and eye damage; may be harmful if swallowed.
Propionic acid	Flammable; may cause skin and eye irritation; harmful if in contact with skin.
Butanol	Flammable; may cause skin and respiratory irritation, and drowsiness or dizziness; may cause serious eye irritation; harmful if in contact with skin.
2-Methylpropanol	Flammable; may cause skin and respiratory irritation, and drowsiness or dizziness; may cause serious eye damage; harmful if swallowed, inhaled, or in contact with skin.
3-Methylbutanol	Flammable; may cause skin irritation, serious eye irritation; harmful if inhaled or in contact with skin.
Butyl acetate	Flammable; may cause skin irritation, and drowsiness or dizziness; may cause serious eye irritation; harmful if inhaled.
Isopentyl acetate	Flammable; may cause skin and respiratory irritation.
Isobutyl propionate	Flammable
Butyl propionate	Flammable; harmful is swallowed; may cause skin irritation, serious eye damage.
Sulfuric acid	May be harmful is swallowed; causes severe skin burns and eye damage.
Sodium carbonate	Harmful is swallowed; may cause mild skin irritation, serious eye irritation.
Sodium chloride	--------
Magnesium sulfate	--------

145

Pre-Lab Study Questions

1. In the Safety Precautions above, there is the suggestion to use sodium bicarbonate for cleaning. What is the rationale for this suggestion?

2. Why must the reaction mixture be cooled before ether is added?

3. What is the purpose of each extraction step? Which layer contains the ester at each step?

Experimental Procedure

Part A Synthesis and Isolation

Step in procedure	Comments

1) Transfer 0.05 mole of alcohol to a 25 mL rbf. Add 0.10 mole of your carboxylic acid.

The alcohol will be given to you in a vial; use the entire amount. Measure the amount by weight (take the difference in weight of the filled and empty vial). The carboxylic acid will be available in a buret. You MUST measure the acid by volume and dispense directly from the buret into the rbf.

2) Carefully add 20 drops concentrated (97%) sulfuric acid and swirl to mix well.

Concentrated sulfuric acid is very corrosive. Wear heavy-duty gloves while handling. If you have contact with it, wash immediately and thoroughly with cold running water. Notify your instructor while you continue to wash.

3) Add a boiling stone. Reflux about one hour and then cool with the condenser in place.

After one hour, the reaction should be close to completion; additional reflux time, if convenient for you, may improve the yield.

4) During the reflux time, prepare 20 mL pre-chilled water for use in the first extraction, steps 7-8.

Take this time to also clean a vial thoroughly and let it air-dry till next week so that you have it ready to store your pure ester after Part B step 3.

5) Disassemble the reflux apparatus; cautiously pour the cool reaction mixture into your separatory funnel, supported in an iron ring.

Be sure always to keep a container beneath the separatory funnel in case of leaking. And be sure the stopcock is closed!

Do not allow the boiling stone to come over into the funnel. It could damage the Teflon stopcock.

6) Rinse the flask with 20 mL ether and add this rinse to the funnel.

7) Add the 20 mL pre-chilled water from step 4.

8) Stopper the funnel; invert it while holding the stopper closed; open the stopcock to vent. Close the stopcock; shake the funnel gently once or twice; vent. Alternate the shaking and venting for several minutes. You may shake more vigorously and vent less often as you proceed.

Frequent venting, especially at the beginning, is necessary to prevent a build-up of internal pressure that could eject the stopper. Point the stem of the funnel away from any person in the lab, including yourself.

Mishaps in performing extractions are the most frequent cause of product loss for this experiment.

9) Separate the layers, and collect the organic layer in an Erlenmeyer flask of at least 125 mL size.

The identity of the organic layer may be deduced from its density relative to water (the density of ether is 0.71 g/ mL). However, a solvent's density is altered by the compounds dissolved in it. You can determine which is organic by mixing a drop of each layer with about a milliliter of water (in two separate test tubes).

10) Use a grease pencil to label the flask with the identity of its contents.

When there are multiple extractions, it is a good idea to identify each layer with a label on its container. In any case, **never throw out any layer from an extraction procedure until the entire experiment is completed**.

11) Perform a series of extractions as described below.

As you perform operations in steps 11-14, replenish the ether to keep the volume of the organic layer approximately constant. Unavoidable loss of the ester product on the surface of the glassware is minimized by dilution.

Rinsing glassware with small amounts of ether in transfer steps improves the efficiency of each transfer and at the same time restores evaporated solvent.

a) To the organic layer slowly and carefully add 10 mL 10% aqueous sodium carbonate, with vigorous stirring until gas evolution stops. Pour the layers into the separatory funnel and continue this extraction in the usual manner.

Carbon dioxide is evolved on contact of a carbonate (or bicarbonate) with acid. Sometimes so much gas is produced that foam can overflow the container. Using sufficiently large glassware and stirring can prevent this.

b) Treat the organic layer again as in step a. Use fresh sodium carbonate solution.

Continue to perform extractions until the <u>aqueous layer</u> is basic to litmus paper (but no less than two times including step a). Sometimes the basification is slow, especially with the higher molecular weight carboxylic acids, so be sure to shake well and allow enough time before testing the pH.

Understanding the chemistry that occurs in the extractions and in the litmus test is essential – see the equations on p. 143.

12) Transfer the ether solution from the separatory funnel to an Erlenmeyer flask of sufficient size that it will be about half full.

Observe carefully – if any water droplets remain, they must be removed using the separatory funnel or careful decanting into a fresh flask.

13) Dry the ether solution with anhydrous magnesium sulfate.

14) Filter the ether solution from the drying agent into a rbf of proper size.

The volume of the solution should be on the order of 25 mL. If less, make it up with ether to this value before filtering. A few rinses of the drying agent with small portions of ether will minimize loss of product.

15) If you have <u>at least</u> 45 minutes left, remove most of the ether by rotary evaporation. Then, transfer the ester to a 10 mL rbf and store it in the drawer, tightly corked, the joint wrapped on the outside with Parafilm. $^{\Sigma}$

Alternatively, if you do not have enough time, you may store the solution in the flask and save as described.

Use a water bath at room temperature. Ether boils at 35 °C and is quickly stripped away.

To evaluate when most of the ether has been removed, begin rotary evaporation with the level of water in the bath equal to that of solution in the rbf. As evaporation proceeds, keep lowering the jack so that the two levels remain equal. Stop when the volume of liquid in the flask does not appear to be noticeably decreasing over a period of a few minutes.

Too vigorous conditions (high bath temperature, long time) could result in some loss of ester as well as ether. It is better to be somewhat cautious.

After the rotary evaporation, a pipet may be helpful in transferring the last few drops into the small rbf.

The small rbf will minimize product loss on the glassware surface during distillation in Part B. The rbf should be about half full or less after the transfer.

For storage, a cork is preferred to a ground-glass stopper, which might "freeze" in place.

If you must stop before this point, be sure to finish at least the first extraction (steps 7-10). After a week's storage of product, it is a good idea to do at least one sodium carbonate extraction unless you have completed the drying step (step 13).

Part B: Purification

Step in procedure	Comments
1) Set up for distillation with water-cooling.	Do not forget the boiling stone.
2) Distil the product.	
a) If you have removed most of the ether by rotary evaporation, begin with a moderate Variac setting; try 70-80 V (or 40-45 %). If you have lots of ether left, you should begin with a low setting such as 50 V (or 30-35 %).	If you are in a drafty area, you may need to insulate the rbf with a tent of aluminum foil.
b) Adjust the Variac so that the rate of distillation is about a drop per second.	
c) Collect the forerun (for later discard).	The forerun is low-boiling material contaminating the desired product or the solvent. You will probably have a forerun, consisting mostly of ether. If no, you should still collect the first few drops separately, which may be an impure ester.
d) <u>Once the boiling point levels off,</u> quickly switch flasks to collect the ester.	A pure material has a constant boiling point, with minor fluctuations (about 1-3 $^{\circ}$C). This fluctuating temperature should be recorded as the boiling range of the liquid. The observed boiling point may not match the literature value, due to thermometer error and/or deviation of atmospheric pressure from standard conditions. A further complication is that if you are distilling a very small volume, the thermometer may never become bathed in liquid-vapor, with the result that the observed boiling point is lower than expected. For these reasons, **do not discard any constant-boiling fraction** – it may be your product.
e) Switch flasks again if the temperature keeps rising instead of becoming level.	A gradually rising temperature usually means a mixture of gradually changing composition is distilling over; that is, the distillate is not pure. In this situation, attempt to obtain one or more fractions enriched in the desired product by changing flasks every time the temperature rises as much as 5 $^{\circ}$C.

f) Stop distilling with some liquid remaining in the pot.

When the volume of liquid in the pot becomes small, the temperature may drop or rise, signaling the end of collection of the main component. **Never distil to dryness** – the residue could ignite or explode.

3) Transfer your pure product to the (pre-weighed) vial in which it will be stored.

Be sure the vial has the plastic domed cap liner that deters evaporation and does not react with the liquid product.

4) Weigh the product.

Describe the odor in your notebook. To observe safe practice, waft the vapors toward your nose as you gently inhale.

At home, determine the overall percent yield.

5) Properly label your vial (your name, date, full name of ester, weight and the observed boiling point range). Depending on which room is more available, proceed to Parts C and D.

Part C Analysis of Product Purity by Infrared Spectroscopy (IR)

Depending on availability of instruments, you may choose to do Part D before C. **Note: Your product will be graded at GC time for label, appearance, and yield. Your product will be collected after you complete both Parts C and D.**

Step in procedure

1) Watch a demonstration of IR techniques.

Comments

Read sections 12.1 and 12.2 for a brief description of FTIR.

2) Take the IR spectrum of your ester neat between salt plates.

Review the instruction on sample preparation in section 12.4. Important: After pre-cleaning with ligroin, be sure to rub the plates completely dry with a tissue. Peaks from traces of water from condensation might otherwise appear in the spectrum.

3) Identify functional groups giving rise to peaks above 1600 cm^{-1}.

Functional Groups	Position (cm^{-1})
O-H of water, alcohol	3600-3200
O-H of carboxylic acid	3400-2500
(carbonyl overtone)	3600-3400
alkyl C-H	3000-2800
C=O typical	1720-1710
C=O of ester	1750-1730
C-O	1300-1000

An overtone is a weak band at almost twice the frequency of a strong band. Because of strong absorption in the region around 1700 cm^{-1}, carbonyl compounds often exhibit overtones in the region around 3400 cm^{-1}. Look at sample spectra of authentic compounds to help you distinguish between the appearance of overtones and O-H peaks. You will find helpful examples in section 12.6.

Overtones may be especially prominent in spectra that are too strong, obtained from preparations with too much sample on the salt plates.

4) Compare your spectrum to that of the known ester,[4] shown in Figures E7.1-E7.4.

Part D Analysis of Product Purity by Gas Chromatography (GC)

Note: Your product will be graded at GC time for label, appearance, and yield. Your product will be collected after you complete both Parts C and D.

Step in procedure	Comments
1) Watch a demonstration of GC techniques.	Read section 11.4 for an introduction to GC.
2) Be sure the chromatograph you plan to use is designated for your ester.	For each ester, the instrument settings will be posted, and you should record the appropriate ones in your notebook.
3) One of the CHE 327 staff will inject your sample into the chromatography.	The sample you submit to the CHE 327 staff should be one clear phase. Otherwise, the syringe could become clogged, with expensive breakage resulting. You must remove particles by small-scale filtration – consult your instructor. Also seek advice if your sample is wet or cloudy.
4) Determine the percent purity.	If your "pure" product has significant GC peaks other than the one for the ester, these might correspond to (a) acetone from incompletely drying the syringe; (b) ether or alcohol from poor separation during distillation; and/or (c) unreacted carboxylic acid from inefficient extraction.

---

[4]http://riodb01.ibase.aist.go.jp/sdbs/cgi-bin/cre_index.cgi?lang=eng

IR Spectra of Esters

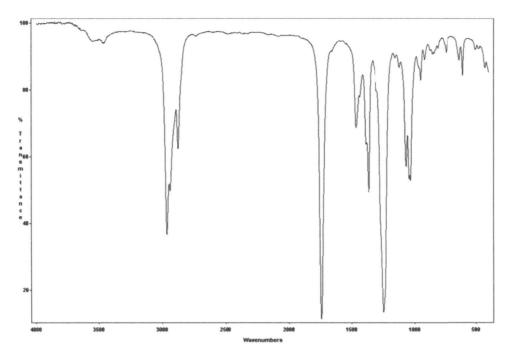

Figure E7.1 IR spectrum of butyl ethanoate.

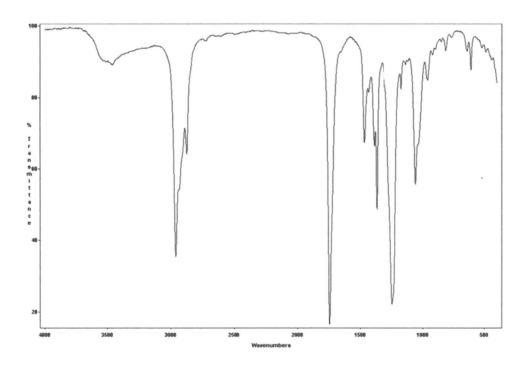

Figure E7.2 IR spectrum of 3-methylbutyl ethanoate.

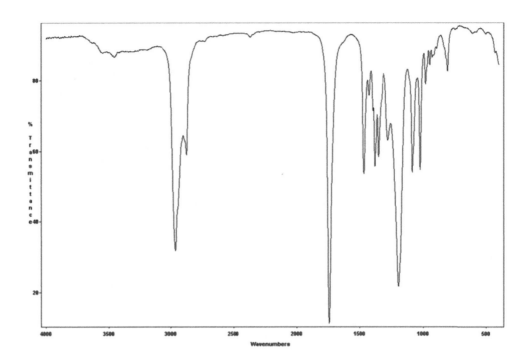

Figure E7.3 IR spectrum of 2-methylpropyl propanoate.

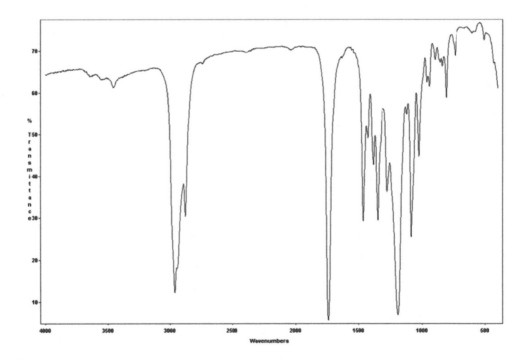

Figure E7.4 IR spectrum of butyl propanoate.

End-of-Lab Checklist

Save	Discard
Lab period 1 (Part A):	**Lab period 1 (Part A):**
1) Keep all layers from the extractions, labeled, until you are sure you do not need them.	1) Add a few milliliters of water to the drying agent; the resulting solution goes into the *LIQUID WASTE* container.
2) If you reached the Σ stopping point (Part A step 15), store the crude ester in a rbf of proper size, corked not stoppered, with Parafilm around the outside of the cork.	2) All other water solutions go into the same *LIQUID WASTE* container.
3) If you stop at some point between Part A steps 11 and 14, store the ester solution in a corked flask. However, you must plan so that you are not stopping at a point where carbon dioxide is still being evolved – the cork could pop off.	
Lab period 2 (Parts B-D):	**Lab period 2 (Parts B-D):**
1) Save other distillation fractions in corked flasks or test tubes until you are sure you do not need them.	At the end of the experiment, all the solutions that are not useful should go into *LIQUID WASTE* container.
2) If you used aluminum foil for tenting, save it in case you need it for the next experiment.	

Post-Lab Study Questions

1. Where does the carbon dioxide come from in Part A step 11?

2. What does a basic litmus test result for the aqueous layer tell you about the ether layer? Explain.

3. Since the product will be purified by distillation, why is so much trouble taken to remove unreacted starting material in the extractions?

4. How can you tell the following sample of 2-methylpropyl propanoate is impure? What is the impurity?

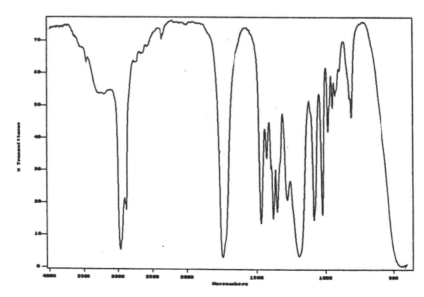

CHE 327 ESTER RESULT FORM (PAGE 1 OF 2) 2017-2018

Student's name______________________________ **TA's name**______________________

Grade_________

Staple your IR spectrum and GC chromatogram to the back of this form.

Fill in:

1. Ester synthesized _________________________________

2. Weight of product **submitted in the vial**________________

   Theoretical yield **in grams**__________ Overall **percent yield**__________

   (Show your complete percent yield calculation below. Clearly identify the limiting reagent. Watch significant figures.)

3. Boiling point (or range) of product **submitted in the vial** ________________________

4. List the major functional groups detected by IR - give the names of the functional groups and the corresponding wave numbers observed.

5. **Answer the following questions. Keep explanations succinct (no more than 30 words).**

   a) Based **only** on the observed boiling point (or range), was the compound obtained the specific ester you attempted to synthesize? Explain.

(Continue on Page 158.)

Student's name_____   **TA's name**_____

b) Based **only** on the functional groups detected in IR, was the compound obtained the specific ester you attempted to synthesize? Explain.

c) How did you tell if the compound obtained was the specific ester you attempted to synthesize? Explain.

(For the use of graders only)

Label/ID _____   Appearance GOOD   OK   POOR

Yield OK   LOW   REFILL/NO PRODUCT   Purity by IR GOOD   OK   POOR

Yield grade_____   Purity by GC GOOD   OK   POOR

Overall Purity grade_____

Experiment 8   MULTI-STEP SYNTHESIS OF LIDOCAINE

Lidocaine (2-diethylamino-N-2',6'-dimethylphenylacetamide) is a common local anesthetic and antiarrhythmic drug. It is also known by various trade names, with Xylocaine being one of the most common names. Its chemical name is 2-diethylamino-N-2',6'-dimethylphenylacetamide. Lidocaine contains an amide functionality as well as a tertiary amine, which is a basic site. Drugs that contain basic sites are often sold as their corresponding hydrochloric or sulfate salts because the salts are usually more stable and compatible with the biological media. Likewise, drugs containing an acidic site (such as aspirin) are converted to the corresponding sodium salts.

Lidocaine

In this experiment, you will prepare lidocaine in a three-step synthesis starting from 2,6-dimethylaniline.

2,6-dimethylaniline   *α-chloro-2,6-dimethylacetanilide*   *lidocaine*

Table E8.1 Molecular weights and densities of reactants and products.

Compound	MW (g/mole)	Density (g/mL)
α-chloroacetyl chloride	112.9	1.42
α-chloro-2,6-dimethylacetanilide	197.7	-----
diethylamine	73.1	0.71
2,6-dimethylaniline	121.2	0.98
lidocaine	234.3	-----
lidocaine bisulfate	332.4	-----

Background Reading

1. Lab period 1 (Parts A-B):

   • Review "Reflux" (chapter 10)

2. Lab period 2 (Parts C-D):

   • Read "Small-scale crystallization" (section 7.4).

   • Review "Acid-Base Extraction" (section 9.3).

3. Lab period 3 (Parts E-F):
    - Review "Crystallization" (section 7.3).

Properties of New Materials

Name	Appearance	Properties	Hazard Statements
2,6-Dimethylaniline	Light purple liquid	Melting Point 11 °C	Combustible; harmful if swallowed, in contact with skin or if inhaled; may cause skin and respiratory irritation; suspected of causing cancer.
α-Chloroacetyl chloride	Colorless liquid	Boiling Point 106 °C	Toxic if inhaled, swallowed or in contact with skin; causes severe skin burns and eye damage; causes damage to organs if inhaled.
Half-saturate sodium acetate solution	Clear liquid	--------	May be harmful if swallowed or inhaled; causes mild skin irritation and eye irritation.
α-Chloro-2,6-dimethylacetanilide	White solid	Melting Point 145-146 °C	May be harmful if swallowed or inhaled; may cause respiratory irritation; causes skin irritation and serious eye irritation.
Lidocaine	White solid	Melting Point 68-69 °C	Harmful if swallowed.
Diethylamine	Yellow liquid	Boiling point 55-56 °C	Flammable; harmful if inhaled or swallowed; toxic if in contact with skin; causes skin irritation and serious eye damage; may cause allergic skin reaction; may cause allergy or asthma symptoms or breathing difficulties if inhaled.
Toluene	Colorless liquid	Boiling point 111 °C	Highly flammable; may be fatal if swallowed and enters airways; causes skin irritation; may cause drowsiness or dizziness, and damage to organs through prolonged or repeated exposure; suspected of damaging fertility or the unborn child.

Pre-Lab Study Questions

1. Lab period 1 (Parts A-B):

   a. Why does HCl evolve during the reaction of 2,6-dimethylaniline and α-chloroacetyl chloride?

   b. What is the purpose of adding sodium acetate at the end of the reaction?

   c. Why do you need to react α-chloro-2,6-dimethylacetanilide with 3 equivalents of diethylamine instead of just one?

2. Lab period 2 (Parts C-D):

   a. In Part C steps 2a-b, what is the purpose of washing the organic layer with water?

   b. What is the purpose of the subsequent extraction with acid?

Experimental Procedure

Part A Synthesis and Isolation of α-chloro-2,6-dimethylacetanilide

| 2,6-dimethylaniline | α-chloroacetyl chloride | | α-chloro-2,6-dimethylacetanilide |

Step in procedure	Comments
1) To a 250-mL Erlenmeyer flask, add 3.0 mL 2,6-dimethylaniline.	The amine will be available in a buret. Make sure to read the label and dispense from the correct buret. **CAUTION: 2,6-dimethylaniline is toxic and easily absorbed through the skin. Wear gloves while dispensing from the buret.**
2) Dissolve the 2,6-dimethylaniline by adding 15 mL glacial acetic acid, followed by swirling the mixture.	**Complete this step, as well as steps 3-5 in the hood.**
3) To the solution from step 2, add 2.0 mL α-chloroacetyl chloride and swirl vigorously.	The reagent will also be available in a buret. **CAUTION: α-chloroacetyl chloride is toxic and corrosive. Wear gloves while dispensing from the buret. If you have contact with it, wash immediately with plenty of soap and water (the alkaline soap will help neutralize the HCl evolved when the acid chloride is hydrolyzed).**
4) In one portion, add 25 mL half-saturated sodium acetate solution to the reaction mixture.	Precipitation of the amide should occur instantaneously upon addition of the sodium acetate solution. Smoke may be observed. The flask will become warm. **CAUTION: HCl gas is generated during the course of the reaction. Avoid inhalation!**
5) Add 60 mL cold water (pre-chilled in an ice-water bath) to the reaction mixture, and stir thoroughly.	Smoke may be observed.
6) Collect the solid by vacuum filtration until drops of water are no longer coming through.	Pour in small portions to avoid overflowing. Use a spatula to scrape out any solid that remains in the flask.
7) Wash the filter cake with a total of 50 mL cold water in small portions. Keep drawing air by vacuum filtration until drops of water are no longer coming through.	Remove the pinch clamp before adding water to maximize the washing effect. Then, reapply pinch clamp to drain the water. Prior to washing, you can also use some of the water to rinse the Erlenmeyer flask to help remove any remaining solid.

162

8) Place a dry filter paper on top of the solid and, using a small beaker, press down on the solid. Keep drawing air by vacuum filtration for at least 5 minutes.

Press down as firmly as you can. If the filter cake cannot be pushed down any further, you may stop. Do not use excessive force, as you may inadvertently break your funnel and/or flask.

9) Remove the solid from the funnel and spread it out over a large weighing paper. Use a spatula to grind up any clumps of solid.

If you performed steps 8 and 9 properly, your solid should be dry enough to transfer into another flask without it sticking to the paper and sides of the flask.

10) Pre-weigh a clean, dry 100 mL rbf.

11) Transfer your product (from step 9) into the rbf.

12) Obtain the weight of your rbf containing your product.

13) Move on to Part B.

Part B Synthesis of Lidocaine

α-chloro-2,6-dimethylacetanilide   diethylamine   lidocaine (crude)

Step in procedure

1) Add 30 mL toluene to the rbf.

Comments

Using a pipette, rinse the inside of the rbf neck and the sides of the flask with the first few mL of toluene to wash down any solid that may be stuck on the sides of the flask.

2) Add a magnetic stirring bar to the rbf.

Obtain the magnetic stirring bar from the stockroom.

3) Add 7.5 mL diethylamine to the rbf.

The reagent will be provided in a buret.

4) Attach a condenser to the flask and set up for heating under reflux. Place the heating mantle on top of a stirring plate.

5) Turn on the stirring plate to begin stirring the suspension.

You may need to set the stirring setting at the highest speed initially because the magnetic stirring bar may be buried underneath the solid in the rbf. Once you begin heating the rbf, the solid will gradually dissolve and your stirring bar will be free to begin stirring the solution.

6) Heat the suspension under reflux for 1 hour.

Set the Variac at about 50 volts (or 30-35%). Foaming may occur during reflux.

7) Allow the solution to cool and disassemble the reflux apparatus.

8) Carefully cover your rbf with a cork and wrap the cork and rbf neck with Parafilm. Carefully place the rbf containing the solution in your drawer.$^{\Sigma}$

Part C Isolation of Lidocaine

Step in procedure

Comments

1) Transfer the solution from your rbf to a separatory funnel.

Reduce mechanical losses by using a stemmed funnel and rinsing the sides of the rbf with toluene as you are pouring the solution into the separatory funnel.

2) Perform a series of extractions as described below:

Keep track of which layers you collect. Make sure to label all your flasks and DO NOT THROW ANYTHING AWAY UNTIL YOU ARE FINISHED. Understanding the chemistry that occurs in these extractions is essential.

a) Wash the organic layer with 50 mL water. **SHAKE GENTLY** to avoid forming an emulsion.

b) Drain the aqueous layer and leave the organic layer inside the separatory funnel.

Use good judgment on when to stop draining. Since you will be washing with water again, it makes more sense to leave a little of the aqueous layer inside the separatory funnel, rather than drain a little of the organic layer.

c) Repeat steps 2a-b three more times (using fresh water each time to wash the organic layer). You will have washed with a total of 200 mL water by the end of this step.

On the final washing step, make sure to drain the entire aqueous layer. It is better to sacrifice some of your organic layer to ensure that only the organic layer remains in your separatory funnel.

d) From the organic layer inside the separatory funnel, extract with 20 mL of a 3 M hydrochloric acid solution. Collect the aqueous layer in a 250-mL Erlenmeyer flask.

Wear heavy-duty gloves. You may shake more vigorously during this extraction. If an emulsion forms, add more toluene to the funnel.

IMPORTANT: Make sure that you do NOT allow any of the organic layer to drain into your Erlenmeyer flask. Do NOT collect any emulsion that may have formed

e) From the organic layer, extract with 20 mL of water and collect the aqueous layer.

Once again, make sure that the organic layer does not enter the collecting flask. If it does, pour the entire contents back into the separatory funnel and drain again.

3) Combine the two aqueous extracts from steps 2d and 2e in the 250-mL Erlenmeyer flask. Cool the solution by placing the flask in an ice-water bath.

4) Add 5 mL of a 3 M sodium hydroxide solution.

Keep the flask in an ice-water bath with swirling throughout the entire addition of 3 M NaOH

5) Keep adding the basic solution in pipetteful increments until the solution becomes strongly basic.

Add a total of ~20 mL (including the 5 mL from the previous step) before testing the solution with litmus paper.

6) Allow the flask, containing the precipitated solid, to sit in the ice-water bath for 5-10 minutes.

Prepare for vacuum filtration during this time.

7) Collect the solid by vacuum filtration. Wash the filter cake with 25 mL cold water.

Use some of the cold water to help remove any of the remaining solid in the Erlenmeyer flask. Remember to remove the vacuum when adding water to the filter cake, and then reapplying the vacuum to drain.

8) Keep drawing air by vacuum until drops of water are no longer coming through.

9) Place a dry filter paper on top of the solid and, using a small beaker, press down on the solid. Keep drawing air by vacuum filtration for at least 5 minutes

Use the same techniques as you did in Part A steps 8-9 in these next two steps.

10) Remove the solid from the funnel and spread it out over a large weighing paper. Use a spatula to grind up any clumps of solid.

11) Carefully set aside 0.25 g of your product in your for Part D, and place the rest in your drawer and allow it to dry until the next lab period.$^{\Sigma}$

12) On the due date, weigh your dry crude lidocaine product, and submit it in a properly labelled vial to your TA.

After class, calculate the percent yield of the entire synthesis.

Part D Small-scale Crystallization of Lidocaine

crude   → crystallization using hexane →   pure

Step in procedure	Comments
1) Place 0.250 g of your crude lidocaine product (from part C) into a large test tube.	If you have less than 250 mg of lidocaine, go to the stockroom for a refill.
2) Set up a water bath in a large beaker and place it on a hot plate. Begin heating the water bath.	You will share the water bath with one other student. The water bath will not need to reach boiling temperature. A warm water bath will be sufficient for this experiment.
3) Add approximately 0.5 ml hexane to the test tube containing the crude lidocaine. Add a boiling stick to the test tube.	
4) Heat the test tube gently in the water bath and swirl until all the solid has dissolved. Immersing only the bottom half of the test tube will be sufficient in heating the solution.	The appropriate amount of solvent for a given weight of solid will vary with the system. Usually it is determined by adding solvent gradually (dropwise, usually) and boiling until the solid just dissolves (the saturation point).
5) Remove the boiling stick and allow the solution to cool to room temperature undisturbed and then to ice temperature.	
6) Remove the solvent using a pipet.	Refer to the *Trimyristin* experiment for the procedure.

7) Leave the test tube open over the week for the product to dry. $^{\Sigma}$

You can try gently tapping the test tube on its side to spread out the solid along the walls of the test tube. Increasing the surface area here will help the drying process.

8) Determine the melting point of your crude and crystallized lidocaine simultaneously.

9) Weigh your product and transfer it to a properly labeled vial. Submit the vial to your TA.

After class, determine the percent recovery of crystallized lidocaine from crude lidocaine.

End-of-Lab Checklist

Save	Discard
Lab period 1 (up to Part B step 9):	**Lab period 1 (up to Part B step 9):**
Place the rbf containing the reaction mixture in your drawer.	At the end of the experiment, all the solutions that are not useful should go into the *LIQUID WASTE* container. The weighing papers and filter papers used should go into the *SOLID WASTE* container.
Lab period 2 (up to Part C step 11; up to Part D step 9):	**Lab period 2 (up to Part C step 11; up to Part D step 9):**
1) From Part C step 11, let the solid dry on a large weighing paper. 2) From Part D step 9, let the crystals dry in the test tube.	At the end of the experiment, all the solutions that are not useful should go into the *LIQUID WASTE* container. The weighing papers and filter papers used should go into the *SOLID WASTE* container.

Post-Lab Study Questions

1. Lab period 1 (Parts A-B):

    a. Why does 2,6-dimethylaniline attack the carbonyl carbon instead of the alkyl carbon?

    b. Why does the addition of sodium acetate result in precipitation of the product?

    c. What would be the effect on the product from step 2 if only one mole of diethylamine (per mole of α-chloro-2,6-dimethylacetanilide) were used in Part B?

2. Lab period 2 (Parts C-D):

    a. What side reaction(s) would be expected if α-chloro-2,6-dimethylacetanilide were still wet when the reaction with diethylamine was performed?

CHE 327 LIDOCAINE SYNTHESIS RESULT FORM 2017-2018 (PAGE 1 OF 2)

Student's name______________________________ **TA's name**______________________

Grade_________

Hand in to your TA your crude lidocaine and purified lidocaine in two separate, properly labeled vials.

Fill in:

1. Weight of crude lidocaine **being submitted in the vial**________________
2. The observed m.p. of your crude lidocaine ________________
3. Weight of crystallized lidocaine **being submitted in the vial**________________
4. The observed m.p. of your crystallized lidocaine __________________

(For the use of graders only)

Crude Lidocaine

Label/ID ______________________________ Yield GOOD OK POOR

Yield OK LOW NO PRODUCT

Yield grade____________________________ Overall Purity grade________________

Crystallized Lidocaine

Label/ID ______________________________ Appearance GOOD OK POOR

Yield OK LOW REFILL NO PRODUCT MP ____________________________

Yield grade____________________________ Overall Purity grade________________

(Continue on Page 170.)

Student's name_____   **TA's name**_____

5. Calculate the <u>overall</u> percent yield of the synthesis to produce crude lidocaine, based on the amount of crude lidocaine you received in Part C step 12. Show work.

6. Based on appearance and melting point data, is your crystallized lidocaine pure? Explain. (**Keep explanation succinct 20-30 words**)

Appendix

PERCENT RECOVERY AND PERCENT YIELD

Percent recovery is a measure of success for a process in which no chemical reaction has occurred, for example, a crystallization or extraction:

$$\text{Percent recovery} = \frac{\text{weight recovered}}{\text{weight used}} \times 100\%$$

Like percent recovery, **percent yield** compares the amount of product to the amount of starting material. In contrast to percent recovery, percent yield factors in the change in molecular weight that generally occurs when a chemical reaction takes place. Because of this change, it is not useful to make a direct comparison of product weight to reactant weight.

To calculate percent yield, start with the balanced equation. You must know the amounts of all reactants in moles or the equivalent. Moles can be found from weight and molecular weight for a pure substance, or from volume and either molarity or percent for a solution.

In all calculations, pay attention to significant figures.

Example 1

A	+	2 B	→	C	+	D
MW 100 g/mole		*MW 110 g/mole*		*MW 108 g/mole*		*etc.*
Wt 5.20 g		*Wt 15.04 g*		*Wt 4.52 g*		
Moles 0.0520		*Moles 0.137*		*Moles 0.0419*		

The equation says that each mole of A requires two moles of B for complete reaction. Therefore, 0.0520 mole A requires 0.104 mole B. The amount that is used, 0.137 mole, is greater than that required, so **A is the limiting reagent**. According to the equation, one mole of C is formed per mole of A, so the theoretical value (maximum that can be formed) for C is 0.0520 mole.

To determine the percent yield of a product, divide the actual moles obtained by the theoretical moles, and convert to percent.

$$\text{Percent yield} = \frac{0.0419}{0.0520} \times 100\% = 80.6\%$$

Example 2

A	+	2 B	→	C	+	D
MW 100 g/mole		*MW 110 g/mole*		*MW 108 g/mole*		*etc.*
Wt 5.20 g		*Wt 10.05 g*		*Wt 4.52 g*		
Moles 0.0520		*Moles 0.0914*		*Moles 0.0419*		

One mole of A requires two moles of B, so 0.0520 mole A require 0.104 mole B. However, only 0.0914 mole B is used. Therefore, **B is the limiting reagent**, even though the weight of B is greater than that of A. The theoretical value for C in this case is ½ (0.0914) = 0.0457. The percent yield is 91.7%.